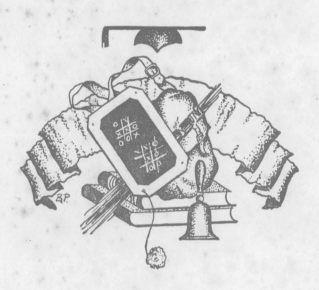

To You
MR·CHIPS
by
JAMES HILTON

HODDER & STOUGHTON
MCMXXXVIII

| FIRST PRINTED | . | . | . | JUNE 1938 |
| REPRINTED | . | . | . | . | JULY 1938 |

*Made and Printed in Great Britain for
Hodder and Stoughton Limited by
Hazell, Watson & Viney Ltd., London and Aylesbury.*

To You
MR·CHIPS

Contents

BIP·PARES·

I
A·CHAPTER·OF AUTOBIOGRAPHY

I

IF I use the word "I" a good deal in these pages, it is not from self-importance, but because I would rather talk about my own schooldays than generalise about schools. Schooling is perhaps the most universal of all experiences, but it is also one of the most individual. (Here I am, generalising already!) No two schools are alike, but more than that— a school with two hundred pupils is really two hundred schools, and among them, almost certainly, are somebody's long-remembered heaven and somebody else's hell. So that I must not conceal, but rather lay stress on the first personal pronouns. The schools I write of were *my* schools; to others at the same schools at the same time, everything may have been different.

I went to three schools altogether—an elementary school, a grammar-school, and a public-school. I matriculated at London University and spent four years at Christ's College, Cambridge. Thus, from the age of six, when my mother led me through suburban streets for presentation to the headmistress of the nearest Infants' Department, up to the age of twenty-three, when I left Cambridge supposedly equipped for the world and its problems, the process called my education was going on. Seventeen years—quite a large slice out of a life, when you come to think about it. And yet the ways I have earned my living since—by writing newspaper articles, novels, and film scenarios—were not taught me at any of these schools and colleges. Furthermore, though I won scholarships and passed examinations, I do not think I now remember more than twenty per cent. of all I learned during these seventeen years, and I do not think I could now scrape through any of the examinations I passed after the age of twelve.

Nor was there any sort of co-ordination between my three schools and the university. For this, nobody was to blame in a free country. To some extent, I learned what I liked; to a greater extent, my teachers taught me what they liked. In my time I "took," as they say, practically every subject takable. At the elementary school, for instance, I spent an hour a week on "botany," which was an excuse for wandering through Epping Forest in charge of a master who, in his turn, regarded the hour as an excuse for a pleasant smoke in the open air. The result is that Botany to me to-day stands for just a few words like "calyx," "stamen," and "capillary attraction," plus the memory of lovely hours amidst trees and bracken. I do not complain.

Again, at the grammar-school I spent six hours a week for three years at an occupation called "Chemistry," and all these hours have left me with nothing but a certain skill in blowing glass tubes into various shapes. In mathematics I went as far as the calculus, but I do not think I could be quite sure nowadays of solving a hard quadratic equation. Of languages I learned (enough to pass examinations in them) Latin, Greek, French, and German. I suppose I could still read Virgil or Sophocles with the help of a dictionary, but I do not do so, because it would give me no pleasure. My French and German are of the kind that is understood by sympathetic Frenchmen and Germans who know English.

The only school-learning of which I remember a good deal belongs to English Literature, History, and Music; but even in these fields my knowledge is roving rather than academic, and I could no longer discuss with any degree of accuracy the debt of Shakespeare to Saxo-Grammaticus or the statute *De Heretico Comburendo*. In fact, although I am, in the titular sense, a Scholar of my college, I do not feel myself to be very scholarly. But give me a new theory about Emily Brontë or read me a pamphlet about war and peace, and I will tell you whether, in my view, the author is worth listening to. To make up for all I have forgotten, there is this that I have acquired, and I call it sophistication since it is not quite the same thing as learning. It is the flexible armour of doubt in an age when too many people are certain.

What all this amounts to, whether my seventeen years were well spent, whether I am a good or a bad example of what schooling can do, whether I should have been a better citizen if I had gone to work at fourteen, I cannot say. I can only reply in the manner of the youth who, on being asked if he had been educated at Eton, replied: "That is a matter of opinion."

The elementary school was in one of the huge dormitory suburbs of North-east London—a suburb which people from Hampstead or Chelsea would think entirely characterless, but which, if one lived in it for twenty years as I did, revealed a delicate and by no means unlikeable quality of its own. I am still a young man, and I suppose that for the next twenty years people will go on calling me "one of our younger novelists"; but whenever nowadays I pass by that elementary school, I realise what an age it is since I breathed its prevalent smell of ink, strong soap, and wet clothes. Just over a quarter of a century, to be precise, but it cannot be measured by that reckoning. The world to-day looks back on the pre-War world as a traveller may look back through a railway tunnel to the receding pinpoint of light in the distance. It is more than the past; it is already a legend.

To this legend my earliest recollections of school life belong. My father was the head-master of another school in the same town, and

I was a good deal petted and favoured by his colleagues. There were quite a few dirty and ragged boys in the class of seventy or so; the school itself was badly heated and badly lit; schoolbooks were worn and smeary because every boy had to follow the words with his finger as he read—an excusable rule, for it was the only way the teacher could see at a glance if his multitude were all paying attention. He was certainly not to blame because I found his reading lessons a bore. At the time that I was spelling out "cat-sat-on-the-mat" stuff at school, I was racing through Dickens, Thackeray, and Jules Verne at home.

The school curriculum had its oddities. Mathematics was divided into Arithmetic, Algebra, and Mensuration. (Why this last had a special name and subdivision, I have no idea.) Geography consisted largely of learning the names of capes, bays, counties, and county towns. When a teacher once told me that Cardigan Bay was the largest in Great Britain,

I remember asking him promptly what was the smallest. He was somewhat baffled. But I have always been interested in miniature things, and perhaps I was right in supposing that England's smallest bay, were it to be identified, would be worth knowing. This teacher gave me full marks, however, because I attained great proficiency in copying maps with a fine-nibbed pen—a practice which enabled me to outline all the coasts with what appeared to be a fringe of stubbly hairs.

I was not so good at history because, in the beginning, I could not make head or tail of most of it. When I read that So-and-so "gathered his army and laid waste to the country," I could not imagine what it meant. I had heard of gathering flowers and laying an egg, but these other kinds of gathering and laying were more mystifying, and nobody bothered to explain them to me. They remained just phrases that one had to learn and repeat. I was also puzzled by the vast number of people in

history who were put to death because they
would not change their religion; indeed, the
entire fuss about religion throughout history was
inexplicable to a boy whose father played the
organ at a Congregational Church during the
reign of Edward the Seventh.

Since then I have helped to write school
history books and have found out for myself the
immense difficulty of teaching the subject to
children. It is not the words only that have to
be simplified, but the ideas—and if you over-
simplify ideas, you often falsify them. Hence
the almost inevitable perversion of history into a
series of gags, anecdotes, labels—that So-and-so
was a "good" king, that Henry the Eighth had
six wives and Cromwell a wart on his nose,
that the messenger came to Wolfe crying "They
run, they run" and that Nelson clapped the
glass to his sightless eye. When later I studied
history seriously for a university scholarship, I
was continually amazed by the discovery that
historical personages behaved, for the most part,

with reasonable motivation for their actions and
not like the Marx Brothers in a costume-play.

"Scripture" was another subject I did not
excel at. It consisted of a perfunctory reading
of a daily passage from the Bible; and our
Bibles were always dirty, ragged, and bound
in black. They left me with an impression of a
book I did not want to handle, much less to
read; it is only during the past ten years that I
have read the Bible for pleasure. Our school
Bibles also suffered from too small print; some
of the words in the text were in italics and
nobody explained to me that the reason for
this concerned scholars more than schoolboys.
Not long ago I heard a local preacher who
seemed to me, when reading from the Psalms, to
give certain sentences an unusual rhythm, and
on enquiry I found that he had always imagined
that the words in italics had to be accented!
Why not print an abridged and large-print Bible
for schools, consolidating groups of verses into
paragraphs, and finally binding the whole

as attractively as any other book? Maybe this has been done, and I am out-of-date for suggesting it.

Another oddity of my early schooldays was something called a free-arm system of hand-writing—it consisted of holding the wrist rigid and moving the pen by means of the forearm muscle. I can realise now that somebody got his living by urging this fad on schoolmasters who liked to be thought modern or were amen-able to sales-talk; I thought it nonsense at the time and employed some resolution in not learning it.

Perhaps the chief thing I *did* learn at my first school was that my father (then earning about six pounds a week) was a rich man. When, later on, I went to schools at which he seemed (in the same comparative sense) a poor man, I had the whole social system already sketch-mapped in my mind, and I did not think it perfect.

The school was perhaps a better-than-

average example, both structurally and educa-
tionally, of its type; so I can only conjecture
what conditions were like at the worst schools
in the worst parts of London. I do know that
there have been tremendous improvements since
those days; that free meals and medical inspec-
tions have smoothed down the rougher differ-
ences between the poor man's child and others;
that, under Hitler and Stalin and Neville
Chamberlain alike, the starved and ragged
urchin has become a rarity. Such a trend is
common throughout the world and we need not
be complacent about it, since its motive is
as much militaristic as humanitarian. But it
does remain, intrinsically, a mighty good thing.
I believe I would have benefited a lot from the
improved elementary school of to-day. I might
not have learned any more, but I should probably have had better teeth.

From the elementary school I went to a
grammar-school in the same suburb. It was an
old foundation (as old as Harrow), but it had

come down in the world. I had the luck to have for a form-master a man who was very deaf. I call it "luck," because he was an excellent teacher and would probably have attached himself to a much better school but for his affliction. As it was, his discipline was the best in the school—with the proviso, of course, that his eyes had to do vigilance for his ears. The result was that, in addition to Latin, English, and History, I gained in his class another proficiency that has never been of the slightest use to me since—ventriloquism.

I was devoted to that man (and I am sure he never guessed it). His frown could spoil my day, his rare slanting smile could light it up. I was conceited enough to think that he took some special interest in me, just because he read out my essays publicly to the class; and after I sent him in an essay I used to picture the excitement he must feel on reading it. It did not occur to me that, like most good professionals (as opposed to amateurs), he did his job conscientiously but without hysterical enthusiasm, and that during out-of-school hours he would rather have a drink and a chat with a friend than read the best schoolboy's essay ever written.

Once he wrote on the blackboard some sentences for parsing and analysis. Among them was: "Dreams such as thine pass now like evening clouds before me; when I think how beautiful they seem, 'tis but to feel how soon they fade, how fast the night shuts in." I was so struck with this that I sat for a long time thinking of it; and presently, noticing my idleness, he asked me rather sharply why I wasn't working. I couldn't tell him, partly because I hardly knew, partly because any answer would have had to be shouted at the top of my voice on account of his deafness. I let him think I was just lazy, yet in my heart I never forgave him for not understanding.

Children are merciless—as much in what they expect as in what they offer. Not only will they bait unmercifully a schoolmaster who lacks the power to discipline them, but they lavish the most fantastic and unreasonable adorations. The utmost bond of lover and mistress is less than the comprehension a boy expects from a schoolmaster whom he has singled out for worship.

I cannot imagine any more desperate situation for a school than the one in which this grammar-school found itself. (It has since moved to another site, so nothing I say can bear any current reflection.) Flanked on one side by a pickle-factory, it shared its other aspects between the laundry of the municipal baths and a busy thoroughfare lined by market-stalls. Personally I rather liked the rococo liveliness of such surroundings. I grew used to the pervading smell of chutney and steaming bath-towels, to the cries of costers selling oranges and cough-drops, and it was fun to step out of the classroom on winter evenings and search a book-barrow lit by naphtha-flares, or listen to a Hindu peddling a corn-cure. And there was a roaring music-hall nearby, with jugglers and Little Tich and Gertie Gitana; and on Friday nights outside the municipal baths a strange-eyed long-haired soap-boxer talked anarchism. Somehow it was all rather like Nijni Novgorod, though I have never seen Nijni Novgorod.

I probably learned more in the street than I did in the school, but the latter did leave me with a good grammatical foundation in Latin, as well as a certain facility in the use of woodworking tools. (Since then I have usually made my own bookshelves.) One of the teachers made us learn three solid pages of Sir Walter Scott's prose from *The Talisman* (a passage, I still remember, beginning—"Beside his couch stood Thomas de Vaux, in face, attitude, and manner the strongest possible contrast to the suffering monarch"); the intention, I suppose, was that we might somehow learn to write a bit more like Scott; but as I did not want to write like Scott at all, the effort of memory was rather wasted.

I worked hard at this grammar-school, chiefly because homework was piled on by various masters acting independently of each other. I was a quick worker, but often I did not finish till nearly midnight, and how the slower workers managed I can only imagine. I have certainly never worked so hard in my life since, and it has often struck me as remarkable that an age that restricts the hours of child-employment in industry should permit the much harder routine of schoolwork by day and homework in the evenings. A twelve-hour shift is no less harmful for a boy or girl because it is spent over books; indeed, the overworked errand-boy is less to be pitied. Unless conditions have changed (and I know that in some schools they haven't), there are still many thousands of child-slaves in this country.

The chief reason for such slavery is probably the life-and-death struggle for examination distinctions in which most schools are compelled to take part. And that again is based on the whole idea of pedagogy which has survived, with less change than one might think, from the Middle Ages. It is perhaps a pity that the average school curriculum fits a pupil for one profession better than any other—that of school-mastering. It is a pity because the clever school-boy is tempted into the only profession in which his store of knowledge is of immediate practical value in getting him a job, and is then tempted to emphasise the value of passing on precisely that same knowledge to others. He is some-what in the position of a shopkeeper whose aim is less to sell people what they need than to get rid of what he has in stock. The circle is vexatious, but I would not call it vicious, be-cause I do not think that the whole or even the chief value of a schoolmaster can be measured by the knowledge he imparts. Much of that knowledge will be forgotten, anyway, and far more easily than the influence of a cultured and liberal-minded personality. Indeed, in a world in which the practical people are so busy doing

things that had better not be done at all, there
may even be some advantage in the sheer mun-
dane uselessness of a classical education. Better
the vagaries of "*tollo*" than those of a new
poison gas; better to learn and forget our Latin
verbs than to learn and remember our experi-
mental chemistry; better by far we should
forget and smile than that we should remember
and be sad.

So I defend (somewhat tepidly) a classical
education for the very reason that so many
people attack it. It is of small practical value
in a world whose practical values are mostly
wrong; it is "waste time" in a world whose
time had better be wasted than spent in most
of its present activities. My Mr. Chips, who
went on with his Latin lesson while the Zeppelins were dropping bombs, was aware that he
was "wasting" the possibly last moments of
himself and his pupils, but he believed that at
any rate he was wasting them with dignity and
without malice.

The War broke out while I was still at the suburban grammar-school; during that last lovely June of the pre-War era, I had won a scholarship to a public-school in Hertfordshire. I remember visiting a charming little country town and being quartered there at a temperance hotel in company with other entrants. The school sent its German master to look after us—a pleasant, sandy-haired, kind-faced man with iron-rimmed spectacles and a guttural accent—almost the caricatured Teuton whom, two months later, we were all trying to hate. I forget his name, and as I never saw him or the school again, I do not know what happened to him.

I never saw the place again because my father, poring over the prospectus, discovered that the school possessed both a rifle-range and an Officers' Training Corps—symbols of the War that, above all things, he hated. He had been a pacifist long before he ever called himself one (indeed, he never liked the term), and it is

literally true to say that he would not hurt a fly—
for my mother could never use a fly-swat if he
were in the same room. Yet I know that if
anyone had broken into our house and attacked
my mother or me—the kind of problem put
two years later by truculent army officers to
nervous conscientious objectors—it would have
been no problem at all to my father; he would
have died in battle. He was no sentimentalist.
When a bad disciplinarian on his teaching staff
once asked him what he (my father) would say
if a boy squirted ink at him, my father answered
promptly: "It isn't what I'd *say*, it's what I'd
do." And he would have—though I cannot
imagine that he ever had to. Boys in his presence always gave an impression of enjoying
liberty without taking liberties. He was a
strong man, physically—a good swimmer, a
good cricketer, nothing of the weakling about
him; and to call him a pacifist is merely to
exemplify his fighting capacity for lost causes.
It never occurred to me then, and it rarely occurs

31

to me now, that any of his ideas were funda-
mentally wrong. He was and happily is still a
mixture of Cobbett and Tagore with a dash of
aboriginal John Bull.

I was just fourteen then—the age at which
most boys in England leave school and go to
work. It was the first autumn of the War, when
our enthusiasm for the Russian steamroller led
us to deplore the fact that we could not read
Dostoievski in the original; so with this idea in
mind, I began to learn Russian and tried for a
job in a Russian bank in London. Worse
still, I nearly got it. If I had, it is excitingly
possible that I should have been sent to Russia
and been there during the Revolution; but far
more probable that I should have added figures
in a City office until the bank eventually went
out of business.

My father, however, was beginning to dally
again with the idea of a public-school for me,
and soon conceived the idea that since he could
not make up his mind, I should choose a school

for myself. So I toured England on this eccentric but interesting quest and learned how to
work out train journeys from York to Chelten-
ham and from Brighton to Sherborne, how to
pick good but cheap hotels in small towns, and
how to convince a headmaster that if I didn't
get a good impression of his school, I should
unhesitatingly cross it off my list. When I look
back upon these visits, I am inclined to praise
my father for a stroke of originality of which
both he and I were altogether unaware. It
would, perhaps, be a good thing if boys were
given more say in choosing their own schools.
It certainly would be a good thing if headmasters cared more about the impressions they
made on boys and less about the impressions
they made on parents. Only a few of the headmasters to whom I explained my mission were
elaborately sarcastic and refused to see me.

Eventually I spent a week-end at Cambridge
and liked the town and university atmosphere
so much that I finally made the choice, despite

the fact that the school there possessed both the rifle-range and the cadet corps. Relying on the fact that my father was both forgetful and unob- servant, I said nothing about this at home, got myself entered for the school, and joined it halfway through the summer term of 1915.

You will here remark that your sympathies are entirely with the headmasters who were sar- castic, and that I must have been an exception- ally priggish youngster. I shall not disagree, except to remark that, prig or not, I am grateful to those pedagogues who showed me over their establishments with as much bored and baffled courtesy as they might have accorded to a foreign general or the wife of a speechday celebrity.

Not so long ago I read a symposium contri- buted by various young and youngish writers about their own personal experiences at public- schools. These experiences ranged from the mildly tolerable to the downright disgusting; indeed, the whole effect of the book was to create

pity for any sensitive, intelligent youngster con-
signed to such environment. I do not for a
moment dispute the sincerity of this symposium.
I am prepared to believe almost any specific
detail about almost any specific school. Of my
own school I could say, for instance, that some
of its hygienic conditions would have aroused
the indignation of every Socialist M.P. if only
they had been found in a Durham or a South
Wales mining village. I could specify, quite
truthfully, that the main latrines were next to the
dining-room; that we were apt to find a drowned
rat in the bath-tub if we left the water to stand
overnight; that in winter the moisture ran down
walls that had obviously been built without a
dampcourse; that the school sanatorium was
an incredible Victorian villa at the other end of
the town, hopelessly unsuited to its purpose.
These things have been remedied since, but
they were true enough in my time—and what
of it? Their enumeration cannot present a
true impression of my school or of any school,

because a school is something more than the buildings of which it is composed.

I know that a visiting American would have been sheerly horrified by the plumbing and drainage, but no more horrified than I am when, having duly admired some magnificent million-dollar scholastic outfit on the plains of the Middle West, I learn that it offers a degree in instalment-selling and pays its athletic coach twice as much as its headmaster. This seems to me the worst kind of modern lunacy. Better to have rats in the bath-tub than bats in the belfry.

I am, as I said just now, prepared to believe almost any specific detail about almost any specific school. But a book or even a page of specific details must be considered with due allowances for the age and character of the writer. Many men after middle-life remember nothing but good about their schools. Their prevalent mood by that time has become so nostalgic for past youth that anything connected

with it acquires a halo, so that even a beating
bitterly resented at the time becomes, in retrospect,
a rather jolly business. (Most of the "jolly"
words for corporal punishment—"spank,"
"whack," etc., were, I suspect, invented by
sentimentalists of over forty.) The kind of man
who feels like this is often the kind that makes a
material success of life and whose autobiography,
written or ghost-written, exudes the main idea
that "school made him what he was"—than
which, of course, he can conceive no higher
praise.

On the other hand, in reading the school
reminiscences of youths who have just left it,
one should remember that the typical schoolboy
is inarticulate, and that by putting any such
reminiscences on paper the writer is proving
himself, *ipso facto*, to be untypical. In other
words, recollections of schools are apt to be
written either by elderly successful men who
remember nothing but good, or by youths who,
by their very skill in securing an audience at

such an early age, argue themselves to have been unlike the average schoolboy.

There is nothing for it, therefore, but to be frankly personal and leave others to make whatever allowances they may think necessary.

I am thirty-seven years of age. I do not think I am old enough yet to feel that school was a good place because I was young in it, or self-satisfied enough to feel that school was a good place because it "made me what I am." (In any case, I do not think it did make me what I am, whatever that may be.) But I enjoyed my schooldays, on the whole, and if I had a son I daresay I would send him to my old school, if only because I would not know what else to do with him.

I was not a typical schoolboy, and the fact that I was happy at (shall we say?) Brookfield argues that the school tolerated me even more generously than I tolerated it. Talking to other men about their schooldays, I have often thought that Brookfield must have been less rigid than many schools in enforcing conformity to type. Perhaps the fact that it was, in the religious sense, a Nonconformist school helped to distil a draught of personal freedom that even wartime could not dissipate. At any rate, I did not join the almost compulsory Officers' Training Corps, despite the fact that the years were 1914-1918. My reasons for keeping out (which I did not conceal) were simply that I disliked military training and had no aptitude for it. Lest anyone should picture my stand as a heroic one, I should add that it was really no stand at all; nobody persecuted me—if they had, no doubt I should have joined.

When later I was called up for military service I responded, chiefly because my friends were in the army and I guessed I should be happier with them there than on committees of anti-war societies with people whose views I mainly held. If this seems an illogical reason, I shall agree, with the proviso that it is also a more civilised reason than a desire to kill Germans.

I did not conceal my views about the War, but I did conceal my general feeling about games. I was, in this respect, a complete hypocrite. I have never been able to take the slightest interest in most games, partly because I am no good at them myself; I like outdoor pursuits such as walking, sea-bathing, and mountaineering, but the competitive excitements of cup-finals and test matches bore me to exasperation. The only contest even remotely athletic into which I ever entered with zest was the saying of the Latin grace at my Cambridge college; it was a long grace, and I was told (how accurately I cannot say) that I lowered the all-time speed record from sixteen to fourteen and a fifth seconds. At Brookfield, however, grace was said by the masters, so that my prowess in this field remained unsuspected, even by myself. The craze for clipping fifths of seconds raged elsewhere. Most of my friends were tremendously concerned about "the hundred yards" and the various School and House matches, and I would not for the world have let them know that I cared nothing about such things at all. Sometimes, if there was absolutely no one else left to fill the team, I took part in some very junior house-match, and I always hoped that my side would lose, because then I should not have to play in any subsequent game. Outwardly, however, I pretended to share all the normal enthusiasms over victory and despairs over defeat; and I think I carried it off pretty well. There is always some ultimate thing you must do when you are in Rome, even if the Romans are exceptionally broad-minded.

I never received corporal punishment at Brookfield; I was never bullied; I never had a fight with anybody; and the only trouble I got into was for breaking bounds. I used to enjoy lazy afternoons at the Orchard, Grant-chester, with strawberries and cream for tea; I liked to attend Evensong at King's College Chapel; I liked to smoke cigarettes in cafés. Most of these diversions were against school rules, and I have an idea that often when I was seen breaking them, the observer tactfully closed an eye. Perhaps it was realised that my desire for personal freedom did not incline me to foment general rebellion. Many things that I care about do not attract others at all, and awareness of this has always made me reluctant to exalt my own particular cravings into the dimensions of a crusade. On the whole, I thought the school discipline reasonable, if occasionally irksome, and when I transgressed I did so without either resentment or regret.

Strangely, perhaps, since I was not "the type," I was quite happy at Brookfield. The very things I disliked (games, for instance) brightened some days by darkening others; I have rarely been so happy in my life as when, taking a hot bath after a football game in which I hardly touched the ball, I reflected that no one would compel me to indulge in such preposterous pseudo-activity for another forty-eight hours. I had many acquaintances, and a few close friends with whom my relationship was as unselfish as any I have experienced since in my life. I do not think I had any particular enemies, and I got on well enough with author, ity. Despite the sexual aberrations that are supposed to thrive at boarding-schools, I never succumbed to any, nor was I ever tempted. I played the piano dashingly rather than accur, ately at Speech Day concerts, breakfasted with the Head once a term, argued for or against capital punishment (I forget which) in the school debating society, and cycled many windy miles along the fenland lanes.

The magic of youth is in the sudden unfolding of vistas, the lifting of mists from the mile-high territory of manhood. It sometimes falls to me nowadays to read a fine new book by a new writer, but never to discover a whole shelf of new books at once—as happened after I had first read *Clayhanger*. New worlds are for the young to explore; later one is glad of a new room or even of a view from a new window.

43

That the worlds were not seen in proper focus, while the room or the view may be, does not entirely compensate for the slowing of excitement—for the loss of a mood in which one hid *The New Machiavelli* inside the chapel hymn-book, or read *Major Barbara* by flashlight under the bedclothes. To such ecstasies youth could add a passionate awareness of being alive, and—during the years 1914–1918—of being alive by a miracle.

Looking back on those days I see that they had an epic quality, and that, after all, the school experiences of my generation were unique. Behind the murmur of genitive plurals in dusty classrooms and the plick-plock of cricket balls in the summer sunshine, there was always the rumble of guns, the guns that were destroying the world that Brookfield had made and that had made Brookfield. Sometimes these guns were actually audible, or we fancied they were; every weekday there was a rush to the newspapers, every Sunday a batch of names read out to stilled listeners. The careful assessments of schoolmasters were blotted out by larger and wilder markings; a boy who had been expelled returned as a hero with medals; those whose inability to conjugate *avoir* and *être* seemed likely in 1913 to imperil a career were to conquer France's enemies better than they did her language; offenders gated for cigarettesmoking in January were dropping bombs from the sky in December. It was a frantic world; and we knew it even if we did not talk about it. Slowly, inch by inch, the tide of war lapped to the gates of our seclusion; playingfields were ploughed up for trenches and drillgrounds; cadetcorps duties took precedence over classroom studies; the school that had prepared so many beloved generations for life was preparing this one, equally beloved, for death.

When I said just now that I disliked military training and had no aptitude for it, I was putting the matter mildly. I dislike regimentation of any kind, and I loathe war, not only for its

pain and misery and life wastage, but for its
enthronement of the second-rate—in men, stand-
ards, and ideals. In the declension of spirit in
which England fought, it is correct to say that
we began with Rupert Brooke and ended with
Horatio Bottomley. But at Brookfield the
loftier mood prevailed even when it was no more
than a Cellophane illusion separating us from
the visible darkness without.

On Sundays we attended Chapel and heard
sermons that, as often as not, preached brotherly
love and forgiveness of our enemies. On
Mondays we watched cadets on the football-
field bayoneting sacks with special aim for vital
parts of the human body. This paradox did
not, I am sure, affect most Brookfield boys as it
did me. To be frank, it obsessed me; I would
wonder endlessly whether Sunday's or Monday's
behaviour were the more hypocritical. I have
changed my attitude since. That Brookfield
declined to rationalise warfare into its code of
ethics while at the same time sending its sons to

fight and die, seems to me now to have been pardonably illogical and creditably inconsistent; looking round on the present-day world of 1938, I can see that countries where high ideals are preached but not practised are at least better off than countries in which low ideals are both preached *and* practised.

Many of us at Brookfield, like myself, were too young—*just* too young—to see actual service in the War; yet during our last school years we lived under the shadow, for we knew or took for granted that if the war lasted we should be illogical and inconsistent in the same English way. Such tragic imminence hardly worried us, but it gave a certain sharpness to all the joys and a certain comfort for all the trivial hardships of school life—gave also, in my own case, the clearest focus for memory. There is hardly a big event of those years that I do not associate with a Brookfield scene; Kitchener's death reminds me of cricketers hearing the news as they fastened pads in the pavilion; the Russian

47

Revolution gives me the voice of a man, now dead, who talked about it instead of giving his usual geography lesson; the *Lusitania* sinking reminds me of early headlines, read hastily over a master's shoulder at breakfast. I composed a sonnet on the Russian Revolution, which my father had the temerity to send to Mr. A. G. Gardiner, eliciting from him the comment that it "showed merit." I also wrote a poem on the *Lusitania* which appeared in the *Cambridge Magazine*, a pacifist weekly run by Mr. C. K. Ogden, who has since distinguished himself by the invention of Basic English. These things I recount, not for vainglory (for they were not particularly good poems), but to reveal something of the mood of Brookfield, in which a boy could be eccentric enough to write poetry and subversive enough to write pacifist and revolutionary poetry without being either persecuted or ostracised. As a matter of fact, I was editor of the school magazine, and wrote for it articles, stories, and poems of all kinds and in all moods.

Nobody tried to censor them; nobody tried to depose or harass me. Looking back on this genial indifference, it seems to me that Brook-field in wartime was not only less barbarian than the world outside it, but also less barbarian than many institutions in what we have since chosen to call peacetime. Is there a school in Soviet Russia where a student may offer even the mildest printed criticism of Stalin? Is there a debating society throughout all Nazi Germany that would dare to allow a Socialist to defend his faith? I suspect that nowadays the boys of Brookfield, members predominantly of the despised bourgeois-capitalist class, are nevertheless free to be Marxian or Mosleyite if they like, and no doubt a few of them are writing wild stuff which in twenty years' time they will either forget or regret. Let us hope, however, that they will not forget the spirit of tolerance which to-day is in such grave peril because it is in the very nature of tolerance to take tolerance for granted.

I do not know whether this spirit obtained at other schools besides Brookfield. Probably at some it did and at others it didn't. But I stress it because the quality of any institution can be tested by the extent to which it withstands attack without compromising too much with the attacker. Granted that during the War all civilised institutions were subtly contaminated, which of them passed such a test most credit-ably? Perhaps we can say that England as a whole, though suffering vast changes, has survived more recognisably than any other country. She is more than the ghost of her former self—she has a good deal still left of the substance. Alone among the countries that participated substantially in the War, her national life is still reasonably well anchored. Mr. Chips, if he were alive (and I have reason to believe he is, in a few schools), could still give the same lessons as in 1908 (not an ideal edu-cational programme, but one that at least attests the durability of a tradition), could still make the

same jokes to a new generation that still under-
stands them, could still offer himself in the
kindly rôle of jester, critic, mentor, and friend.
No upstart authority has yet compelled him to
click his heels and begin the day with juju
incantations of *Heils* and *Vivas*. He can still
say, without fear of rubber truncheons:
" Umph . . . Mr. Neville Chamberlain . . .
umph . . . I used to know his father when he
was the wild man of Born—I mean Birmingham . . . but his sons have turned—umph—
respectable. . . ."

This spirit of free criticism, even if it expresses
itself no more momentously than as a classroom
squib, is the sort of thing that makes English
Conservatives liberal and keeps English Social-
ists conservative. It is the spirit that made
Baldwin protest against Fascist brutality at the
Albert Hall, that gives Citrine misgivings about
Russia, and that united ninety per cent. of Eng-
lishmen in fervent if soon-forgotten admiration
of Dimitrov. It is the spirit that made Mr.

51

Chips protest amidst the bomb explosions:
" These things that have mattered for a thousand
years are not going to be snuffed out because
some stink-merchant invents a new kind of
mischief."

Unfortunately, it looks as if they *are* going to
be snuffed out. Mr. Chips was too valiant an
optimist to face the tragic impasse of the
twentieth century—the fact that civilisation,
because in its higher manifestations it is essentially
organised for peace, cannot long survive war—
even a war supposedly undertaken on its behalf.
There can be no war to end wars, because all
wars begin other wars. There can be no such
thing as a war to save democracy, because all
wars destroy democracy. There could have
been a peace to save what was left of democracy,
but the chance of that came and went in 1919—
the saddest year in all the martyrdom of man.

Here the reader may protest that much of the
above argument depends on the assumption
that England and our institutions deserve to

survive. There was a time when I would not by any means have taken this for granted. It was possible, then, to feel that the pre-War world, having encouraged or permitted a system that led to catastrophe, might as well be destroyed completely to make way for newer and better things. (It was possible, then, to say "newer and better" as glibly as one says "spick and span.") It was possible, then, to decry the public-schools as the bulwark of a system that had had its day, to attack them for their creation of a class snobbery, to lampoon their play-the-game fetish and their sedate philistinism. That these attacks were partly justified one may as well admit. The public-schools *do* create snobbery, or at any rate the illusion of superiority; you cannot train a ruling class without such an illusion. My point is that the English illusion has proved, on the whole, humaner and more endurable, even by its victims, than the current European illusions that are challenging and supplanting it; that the public-school English-

men who flock to a Noel Coward revue to join
in laughs against themselves are patterned better
than the polychromed shirt-wearers of the
Continent who not only cannot laugh but dare
not allow laughter. Granted that the long
afternoon of English imperialism is over, that
dusk is falling on a dominion wider if less solid
than Rome's. Granted that the world is tired
of us and our solar topees and our faded kip-
lingerie, that it will not raise a finger to save us
from eclipse. Time will bring regrets, if any.
For myself, I do not object to being called a
sentimentalist because I acknowledge the passing
of a great age with something warmer than a sneer.

But the accusation of sentimentality comes
oddly from those who extol the Russian collect-
ivist as Rousseau extolled the noble savage. In
some circles to-day it is even fashionable to decry
the more literate occupations altogether and to
redress the undoubted middle-class overweight
in pre-War art by refusing hallmarks to anything
modern that cannot call itself " proletarian."

This forces me to a confession (snobbish if you insist) that in my opinion a man need not be ashamed of having been educated—even at Brookfield and Cambridge. When I reflect on the manner in which the Gadarene pace of 1938 is being set by an ex-house-painter, I do not need to apologise for being an ex-public-schoolboy (comic phrase though it is), and I can even turn with relief to the visionary ideals of a man whose reputation, faded to-day, will bloom again as we remember him more and more wistfully in the years ahead. And Woodrow Wilson was an ex-schoolmaster.

Let history write the epitaph—England, liberalism, democracy were not so bad—not so good, either, on all occasions, but better, maybe, in a longer retrospect. Some of us may even survive to make such a retrospect. All over the world to-day the theme and accents of barbarism are being orchestrated, while the technique of mass-hypnotism, as practised by controlled press and radio, is being schooled to construct a façade of justification for any and every excess. The English illusion is dying; "on dune and headland sinks the fire." But there are other and fiercer fires. It is remarkable (if only a coincidence) that the first victims of the new ferocities have been countries in which there is a long tradition of cruelty (Chinese tortures, Ethiopian mutilations, Spanish bull-rings); one is almost tempted to a belief that the soil can be soured by ancestral lusts, and that English freedom from actual warfare within her own territories for two centuries has been, in effect, a cleansing and a purification. Perhaps this is too mystical for proof; perhaps it is just nonsense, anyway. But it is true that violence begets violence, that delight in the infliction of suffering is a poison in the bloodstream of nations as well as of individuals, and that soon we may be faced with the prospect of a world impelled to its doom by sadists and degenerates. In the next war (that is to say, in the war that has already begun) there will be no heroes charging splendidly to death because

" someone has blundered," but grey-faced *mori-turi*, prone in their steel coffins, diving to kill and be killed because, in the reckoning of authority, no one has blundered at all.

Do not think I am blind to the faults of the age of which Mr. Chips and his type were the product as well as the makers. Its imperialism was, at its worst, smug, hypocritical, and preda-tory. Its *laissez-faire* capitalism resulted in such horrors as child-slavery in factories. Its vices were as solid as its virtues. But one fact does emerge from any critical analysis of the period beginning, roughly, with the Queen's accession and ending with her death—that it was possible, during this time, for an intelligent man in West-ern Europe to look around his world and believe that it was getting better. He could see the spread of freedom, in thought and creed and speech, and—even more important—the spread of the belief that such an increase of freedom was an ultimate goal, even if it could not be im-mediately conceded. He could watch the transplantation of parliamentary government into lands where, though it might not wholly suit the soil, few doubted it would eventually flourish. He could believe that mechanical inventions were spreading civilisation because the chief mechanical invention of the time, the railway, was not (like the aeroplane) diabolically apt for use in warfare. He could observe each year new sunderings of barriers between lands until traveller and student could roam through Europe more freely than at any time since the break-up of Christendom.

True that the boy Dickens toiled in a blacking-factory, but he grew up free to scarify the system that had forced him to it; he had been a child-slave, but he was never a man-slave. True that Huxley was attacked for teaching that men and monkeys were somewhat the same; but he was never exiled for refusing to teach that Jews and Gentiles were altogether different. Scientists may have incurred the wrath of bishops for spreading what the latter considered to be evolutionary nonsense; they were never ordered by government to teach what every acknowledged authority considers to be Aryan nonsense. And while Karl Marx laboriously constructed his time-bomb to explode the bourgeoisie, his victims rewarded him with a ticket to the British Museum instead of a Leipzig trial, and a peaceful grave in Highgate Cemetery instead of a trench in front of a firing-squad.

Occasionally throughout the ages, the clouds of history show a rift and through it the sun of human betterment shines out for a few deceptive moments over a limited area. The Greece of Pericles was one such time and place; parts of China under certain dynasties offered the spectacle of another; Paraguay under the Jesuit Communists was perhaps a third. These few have little in common save a crust of security over the prevalent turbulence of mankind; the crust was thin and its promise of permanence false. But Victorian England sealed the volcano more stoutly than it had ever been sealed

before, so that a man and his son and his son's
son might live and die in the belief that the
world would not witness certain things again.
The crust, indeed, was such that even after the
first shattering its debris is something to cling to
—until the next.

All of which may sound a huge digression in
a book dedicated to the memory of an old schoolmaster.   But for me it is not so.   I cannot think
of my schooldays without the image of that incredible background—Zeppelins droning over
sleeping villages, Latin lessons from which boys
stepped into the brief lordliness of a second-
lieutenancy on the Somme.   I cannot forget the
little room where my friends and I fried sausages
over a gas-ring and played George Robey
records on the gramophone, and how, in that
same little room with the sausages frying and the
gramophone playing, one of us received a telegram with bad news in it, and how we all tried
to sympathise, yet in the end arrived at no better
idea than to open a hoarded tin of pineapple

chunks to follow the sausages. I cannot forget cycling so often over the ridge of the Gog-magogs (which, as Mr. Chips always informed us, was the highest land between Brookfield and the Ural Mountains), and the soft fenland rain beginning to fall on Cambridge streets at dusk, with old men fumbling in and out of bookshops, and young men, spent after route-marches, scampering over ancient quadrangles. Those days were history, but most of us were too young to be historians, too young to disassociate the trivial from the momentous—gnarled desks and war-headlines, photogravure generals and the school butler who stood at the foot of the dormi-tory staircase and at lights-out warned sepul-chrally—"Time, Gentlemen, Time." It was Time in a way that so many of us could not realise. That warning marked the days during which, on an average, ten thousand men were killed.

Mr. Chips would walk between the lines of

beds in the dormitory and turn out the lights.
He was an old man then, and it was impossible
to think he had ever been much younger. He
seemed already ageless, beyond the reach of any
time that could be called. Schooldays are a
microcosm of life—the boy is born the day he
enters the school and dies the day he leaves it;
in between are youth, middle-age, and the elderly
respectability of the sixth-form. But outside
this cycle stands the schoolmaster, watching the
three-year lifetimes as they pass him by, remembering faces and incidents as a god might
remember history. An old schoolmaster, if he
is well-liked and has dignity, is rather like a god.
You can joke about him behind his back, but
you must acknowledge him to his face while you
love him a little carelessly in your hearts. This
has been the relationship of good men and good
gods since the world began.

There was no single schoolmaster I ever knew
who was entirely Mr. Chips, but there were

several who had certain of his attributes and achieved that best reward of a well-spent life—to grow old beloved. One of them was my father. He did not train aristocrats to govern the Empire or plutocrats to run their fathers' businesses, but he employed his wise and sweetening influence just as valuably among the thousands of elementary schoolboys who knew and know him still in a London suburb.

2

GERALD *and the* CANDIDATE

E

2

GERALD was eight when he first went
to stay with Uncle Richard. He had no
parents, and the frequent prep./school
holidays had to be filled up somehow; that was
the reason. He was a quiet boy, full of dreams.
For weeks during the winter term at Grayshott
(which was the prep./school for Brookfield) he
had talked to Martin Secundus about the visit: "I
say, Martin, I'll have to go into training—Uncle
Richard always takes people such long walks
when they go and stay with him. He's a great

explorer, you know. Once he was nearly killed in the jungle by a tiger. He can climb any mountain there is. And he lives in an old castle with a moat round it, and before you can get in you have to give the password."

Actually Gerald had never seen Uncle Richard or where he lived. Everything was new to him—the house and the town and the kind of country, the journey there in the train that went "You-can-if-you-like — You-can-if-you-like," and not just "No, you mustn't — No, you mustn't," like the local train to Grayshott; and the first meeting at twilight on Browdley station platform with Uncle Richard. The platform was made of wooden planks, and as Gerald walked along it the thump—thump—thump made him think of his second favourite "pretend"—that he was a great general, marching at the head of soldiers—"Follow me, my men!" But he was soon back at his chief and almost permanent "pretend"—that he was the engine-driver of the Scotch express, which was half an hour late with the King and Queen on board, and the King had said to the stationmaster: "My good fellow, I *must* arrive in time," and the stationmaster had answered: "Well, your Majesty, that's going to be a difficult matter, but we have one man, Gerald Holloway, whom we can try. If anyone can get you there, he will." Steadily, steadily, throughout the night, a hand always on the throttlelever, eyes peering ahead . . . that was how it went on. Very often the King knighted him as the station clock struck the hour at which the train was due to arrive.

But this time Gerald hadn't a chance to think as far as that, because of Uncle Richard.

"Well, my boy," said Uncle Richard, in a very loud, gruff voice. Then he arranged with a porter about having Gerald's trunk and tuckbox sent on, and after that began to walk away towards the ticketbarrier. Gerald was sorry to be whisked off the platform so soon; he rather wanted to look at the engine—it was a

Four-Four-Nought. None of the grown-up
people he knew had any idea what a Four-Four-
Nought was; but Gerald considered it quite
everyday knowledge.

"So you're Gerald," said Uncle Richard,
when they came to the street.

Gerald said he was.

"You'll have to speak up a bit, my boy—I'm
a little deaf. Gerald, eh? Well, you've come
here at a lively time, and no mistake." And he
made a noise in his throat which Gerald thought
was like something, if he could only think what.
It sounded like "wuff-wuff." "Yes, a right-
down lively time. Better make a good start,
young shaver, and wear your colours."

Whereat Uncle Richard halted under a lamp
and fished in his pocket, producing after some
search a large red rosette which he stooped and
pinned to the lapel of Gerald's overcoat. Gerald
looked up at him with an interest that suddenly
quickened to excitement. Was it possible that
here, at last, was a grown-up who knew the

things that really mattered in the world ? From
that moment, at any rate, he was aware that
Uncle Richard was not to be classed with any
other people. He smiled, privately to himself,
and then with open friendliness at the big face
that overtopped his own.

"There you are, my boy. Red's for Liberal.
Consequently is, the folks'll know what you
are."

Gerald did not understand this at all, but he
was quite contented as he trotted along. He
knew he was going to like Uncle Richard.

Uncle Richard lived at Number 2, The
Parade, which was the best house in Browdley's best street—a double pre-eminence signalised
by the fact that none of the other streets in Browdley had front gardens, and none of the other front
gardens in the Parade was as big as Uncle
Richard's. His, indeed, was about the size of a
railway waiting-room, and nothing grew in it
except some evergreens that were really ever-
black. Nevertheless, the social gulf proclaimed

by them and by their cindery soil was immense. They made the Parade the Park Lane of Browdley. Uncle Richard's was the end house of a row of twelve—grimy, bay-windowed, and ornamented in the most florid mid-Victorian style; and Browdley, in point of fact, was just a Northern industrial town of some eight or ten thousand inhabitants, mostly employed in the local industries of iron-founding and calico-printing. In the junior geography form at Grayshott, noisy with talk of capes and bays and county towns and what belonged to whom, the word "Browdley" was unknown. It was the sort of place that nobody ever went to and that nobody had ever heard of.

But that, if he had known anything about it when he was eight, would have seemed to Gerald just a part of the vast grown-up conspiracy to avoid seeing things as they really were. As he and Uncle Richard walked through the streets from the station to the Parade, he was quite sure about Browdley and equally sure about himself in it. With that red rosette in his coat-lapel he was a knight, flaunting his banner and about to do something heroic; and Uncle Richard was clearly another knight; and Browdley was the beautiful and mysterious place where they both had to do whatever it was. The streets of that magic city were glittering with bright windows, and Gerald's eyes, as he walked along, could just peer over the sills and sometimes under the drawn blinds. Wonderful sights—an old man leaning over a fire, a woman peeling potatoes at a table covered with dishes. a little girl sitting on a high stool in front of a piano. Such people might have been seen elsewhere, but they would not have been the same; and that was because he was with Uncle Richard and they were both wearing those red rosettes.

Soon they came to the house. It had a street lamp outside it that shone a green light, and whenever afterwards Gerald mentioned this and Aunt Lavinia said (as she sometimes did):

"What nonsense, Gerald! Did anyone ever see a street lamp with a green light!"—Gerald used to reply: "Well, it *was* a green light, and it made the house look wonderful. And there was a dragon on the front door." Whereupon Aunt Lavinia would usually say: "Don't take any notice of him, Mrs. So-and-so. He *romances*." But there *was* this green light, and the dragon on the front door was the brass knocker, which seemed to Gerald exactly like a dragon.

Uncle Richard unlocked the door with a key and guided Gerald down a dark passage-way, along which there were other doors with strips of light under them, and the sound of voices beyond. Suddenly Uncle Richard opened one. "Well, here's the young criminal!" he said, weighing his hand down on Gerald's shoulder.

Then Gerald looked up and saw what a huge, red face his uncle had, and how hair grew in tufts out of his nose and ears, how thick his fingers were, and how, when he spoke, the light

in the room seemed to blink. And then suddenly he knew what the "wuff-wuff" was
really like—it was like the bark of a big black
dog. "Well, well, here we are, my boy.
This is your Aunt Flo. She'll get you a bite of
supper, and then off you go to bed."

Gerald was rather dashed at that; surely bed
could not be part of this new and marvellous
existence? But Aunt Flo, who wore glasses,
smiled and patted his cheek. "You look tired
after your journey," she said, but Gerald, who
felt anything but tired, did not reply. Then
she shouted to Uncle Richard: "He says he's
tired after his journey"; which was really not
true at all. By that time, however, Gerald was
staring round the room and at everything in it.
It was a very warm red room, with a crackling
fire and a brass rail stretching the whole length
of the mantelpiece over the fireplace. To one
side stood a long dresser, scrubbed white, and on
this there was a queer, dome-shaped object
covered with a dark cloth. "That's Polly,"

said Aunt Flo. " She's gone to bed now and
we mustn't wake her. A parrot, Gerald—have
you never seen a parrot before ? "

Of course he had; he had been to the Zoo.
" Does it talk ? " he asked.

" Yes, she can say ' Give me a nut. You'll
see to-morrow."

Gerald was a little awed at the prospect of
seeing Polly, though he didn't think " Give me a
nut " was much of a thing to say, even for a
parrot. Then he noticed that the room had two
windows, only one of which had a blind drawn
over it; the other looked through into another
sort of room. Now this was a peculiar thing—
so peculiar that he could not help being rude
(for Aunt Lavinia had always assured him that
it was rude to ask questions). " Where does
that lead to, Uncle Richard ? " he said.

" He wants to know what's out there ! "
shouted Aunt Flo.

" Out there, my boy ? Wuff-wuff. Why,
that's the greenhouse. Only we don't use it as

a greenhouse now. It's where I keep my tricycle."

"Tricycle ?"

"Never seen a tricycle ?"

"I've seen a parrot, but I've never seen a tricycle," answered Gerald; so Uncle Richard beckoned him nearer to the window, and there it was, quite plainly—a tricycle. And on the handlebars, as on the lapels of Gerald's and Uncle Richard's coats, there was a red rosette.

Gerald went to bed that night in a whirl of excitement that made him forget to be frightened because of the dark. Once he heard a lot of talking downstairs and Uncle Richard wuff-wuffing in the passage. Then he closed his eyes and thought of Polly and the tricycle, and the King walked up to the engine-cab and said: "Rise, Sir Gerald," and pinned on his coat the biggest red rosette in the world.

In the morning, that first morning at Uncle Richard's, Gerald awoke with a half-fear that it would all be different. But no; when he came

77

downstairs, Uncle Richard was there, looking just as big in the daylight. "Good morning," he began. "I hope you slept with your colours pinned on to your night-shirt." Now this was exactly what Gerald had done, but he had not been going to tell anybody. Marvellous that Uncle Richard should have guessed! "Yes, of course," answered Gerald, and Uncle Richard laughed loudly and then went to look at something on the wall and blew his nose like a trumpet. "Glass is rising—consequently is, my boy, we'll have some fine days for you."

All at once Gerald looked across the room and saw Polly. She was perched inside the cage on a wooden bar, with her head cocked sideways as if she were listening carefully. Oh, what a beautiful parrot! He ran towards her and she began to squawk and ruffle her feathers, which were bright green, with little patches of red and yellow. "Don't frighten Polly," said Aunt Flo. "When she gets to know you she'll let you stroke her, but don't try yet—she might nip." Gerald felt cross at being squawked at; after all, he had only meant to be friendly. So, when Aunt Flo and Uncle Richard were both looking away, he took a pencil out of his pocket and pushed it through the bars of the cage. This made the bird squawk more than ever, but Gerald had time to withdraw and hide the pencil before anyone saw him.

"Now that's very naughty of Polly," said Aunt Flo, coming over and putting her head against the cage. "Gerald's come to see you and you're being very rude, so you shall just go back to bed again." And she grabbed the piece of dark cloth and pulled it down over the cage. "She deserves it," Aunt Flo added, "for being in such a bad humour."

Nobody ever knew that Gerald had poked the parrot with a pencil. It was a secret for as long as the world should last.

There was porridge and a brown egg for breakfast, and afterwards a girl came into the room. Uncle Richard said: "Aha, the gather⁄

ing of the clans. We must introduce you . . .
Olive . . . and Gerald . . . We're going to
put you to work this morning—both of you."

She looked about the same age as Gerald and
had straight yellow hair and blue eyes. He did
not like girls as a rule, but he noticed that she
was wearing the same kind of red rosette, and
immediately he saw what it all meant in a flash
—it was a secret society, and they were all sworn
to help one another, even girls. So he said
politely : " Hello."

Then Uncle Richard told them what he
wanted them both to do. It was a grand adventure. They had to walk along the neighbouring
streets and put a red bill through every letter-box,
giving a double-knock afterwards, like a postman. Gerald had often practised being a postman, so he was overjoyed. If a house hadn't
got a letter-box, then they would have to push the
bill under the front door. It was all most important work, and they must wear their red
rosettes all the time.

So they went out with the bills and began along the Parade. How beautiful the Parade was in the lovely sunshine! Some people asked them inside the houses and gave them sweets and pennies, which only proved to Gerald that real life wasn't a bit like the silly make-believe of being at school. And some day, when he left Grayshott, there would be real life all the time. He was so busy knocking like a postman that he hardly spoke to Olive, except once, when a whistle in the distance reminded him to ask: "Have you ever been faster than sixty miles an hour?"

"We have a horse that can run as fast as that," said Olive.

"A horse as fast as a train?" echoed Gerald scornfully, but he was a little perturbed as well. He just answered, very off-hand: "Oh, a race-horse—that doesn't count"—and let the conversation lapse.

When they had finished giving out the bills they went back to Uncle Richard's, and there

another odd thing happened. A very old lady
was in the passage-way talking to Uncle
Richard and Aunt Flo, and as Gerald and Olive
came in she lifted her spotty veil and stared.
"Yours ?" she said, and Aunt Flo shouted:
"She's asking who they belong to, Richard !"

Uncle Richard answered: "My nephew,
this is—wuff-wuff—and this"—pointing to
Olive—"is the Candidate's little girl."

That was the first time that Gerald ever heard
of the Candidate.

The Browdley by-election was what the news-
papers called "closely contested." Sir Thomas
Barton, a cotton magnate, was opposed by Mr.
Courtenay Beale, a young London barrister
with a superfluity of brains and bounce. Sir
Thomas, wealthy, middle-aged, and a widower,
liked to play the democrat on these occasions;
and as, in any case, there were no good hotels in
Browdley, he found it convenient to lodge with
Uncle Richard during the campaign. In

another sense, of course, he found it highly inconvenient; Number 2, The Parade, seemed a strange habitation after his baronial mansion a hundred miles away. In his own mind he saw Uncle Richard's house as "just an ordinary small house in a row"—he totally failed to perceive the immense social significance of the front garden. And Uncle Richard himself he thought a decent, well-meaning fellow, with some local influence, no doubt—a retired tradesman, wasn't he ?—something of the sort. His wife, too, a good woman—fortunately, too, a good cook. Everything spotlessly clean, of course. And no children—only a little boy staying with them, a nephew—very quiet—one hardly knew he was there. Useful, too, as a playmate for Olive.

All this was remote from the world that Gerald lived in, and however much he probed it by questioning he could not really make it his own.

"Uncle Richard, what is a Candidate ?"

"He wants to know who the Candidate is, Richard!"

" Oho—taking an interest in politics already,
eh ? Wuff-wuff ! Why, he's a Liberal—that's
why we're trying to get him in."

" Get in where ? "

" He wants to know all about him, Richard,
I do believe ! "

" You mean his name ? Well, my boy, he's
called Sir Thomas Barton. Do you know what
' Sir ' means ? "

This time it was Gerald's turn to shout.
" Yes, it means he's a knight."

" Right to a T, my boy. Knighted by the
King—consequently is, you have to call him
' Sir.' Be careful of that, mind, if you should
ever happen to meet him on the stairs."

All of which was tremendous confirmation of
something that Gerald had long suspected—that
he and Uncle Richard were real people, knowing real things. A knight, indeed ! And on
the stairs ! That was how you were liable to
meet knights, but no grown-up except Uncle
Richard had ever seemed to realise it.

"You see," added Uncle Richard, pointing along the passage towards the always closed door of the front parlour, "that's *his* room. Never you go making a noise outside of it, because you might disturb him when he's at work."

"At work?"

"Yes, my goodness, and plenty of it. Didn't I tell you, my boy, he's trying to Get In? And you and me and your Aunt have all got to help him, otherwise the Other Candidate'll Get In!"

This was the first time that Gerald had ever heard of the Other Candidate.

Marvellous, mysterious days. Every morning when he came downstairs Gerald found Uncle Richard still up, and every night when he went to bed Uncle Richard was still down. Was it possible that he never had to go to bed at all? And every morning he tapped the barometer (Gerald knew all about that now) and made some queer remark that was supposed to be funny; at any rate, it made Uncle Richard himself laugh. One morning he said : " Fine day for the race," and Gerald pricked up his ears and said : " What race ? "

Then Uncle Richard's face crinkled up sud⁄denly. " The human race," he answered. He went on laughing at that until Aunt Flo said : " Come and have some breakfast and stop plaguing the boy."

But Gerald wasn't plagued at all. He smiled at Uncle Richard to show that he appreciated the joke, whatever it was, and that, anyhow, he and Uncle Richard were on the same side in the great battle.

The joy of being sure of this sharpened the joy of giving out bills and knocking at doors ; there was also a song that the boys from the streets round about would sing :

> " *A Li⁄ber⁄al Tom Barton is,*
> *And Li⁄ber⁄als are we,*
> *We'll vote for Barton, all of us,*
> *And make him our M.P.*"

Gerald liked this because he knew the tune (it was "Auld Lang Syne"), but he couldn't understand all the words. However, the words of songs never mattered. But he did know that "Tom Barton" was really wrong, so he always sang "Sir Thomas," very quietly to himself, so that he should be right without anyone hearing him.

(And afterwards, when the Candidate had Got In, he would tell people that he owed it all to one person—someone who had helped him by handing out bills, and who had called him by his proper name all the time; moreover, he had a most important engagement in London, and though there was a special train with steam up waiting for him at Browdley station, no one would undertake to drive it fast enough to reach London in time. So Gerald cried out: "*I* will, Sir Thomas . . ." and Uncle Richard waved to him from the platform, as the huge engine—a Pacific Four-Six-Two, by the way—gathered speed . . .)

" Is the Other Candidate a knight ? " he once asked Uncle Richard.

" Eh, what's that ? Wuff-wuff—young Beale a knight ? God bless my soul, no. A little jumped-up carpet-bagger, that's all *he* is."

The strangest things were happening all the time in that enchanted city of Browdley. Houses were decked with blue and red flags (blue, Gerald learned, was the Other Candidate's colour) ; windows were full of bills and cards ; at every street corner in the evenings groups of people gathered, and sometimes a man got up and shouted at them, waving his arms about. Excitement filled the market-place and ran along the streets ; the little brown houses, doors wide open on to the pavements, were alive with eagerness and gossip and the knowledge of something about to happen. Gerald, walking about with Uncle Richard, could sniff the battle of Good and Evil in the air.

" Well, Dick. D'ye think he'll get in ? "

" We're doing our best, Tom."

"It'll be a touch-and-go with him, anyway. T'other Candidate's gaining ground."

"A carpet-bagger, Tom, if ever there was one —a carpet-bagger."

"They do say he's got one o' them motor-cars."

"He *would* have. Anything to make a noise." In the morning the rumour was confirmed. The Other Candidate had a motor-car, and it was one of the very first motor-cars to appear in most of the streets of Browdley. Gerald, in secret, would not have minded looking at it; but because it belonged to the Other Candidate he pictured himself driving an express train and overtaking it, along a parallel road, so quickly that he could hardly see it at all. But, no, perhaps that was too easy. He was riding Uncle Richard's tricycle instead, and even *that* over-took it. And the Other Candidate scowled and shouted after him: "Who will rid me" (like Henry II and Thomas à Becket in the history book) " of this turbulent young man who rides a tricycle so fast that I cannot catch him up in my motor-car?" (Eight knights sprang forward and ran after Gerald, but they could not catch him.)

Actually Gerald spent most of his time in the streets near Uncle Richard's house. Sometimes, if it were raining, he played in the greenhouse; there were red and blue panes of glass in the greenhouse door. If you looked through the red, everything was hot and stormy; if you looked through the blue, it was like night-time. That was very wonderful.

One day he had a tremendous adventure. Browdley lies in a valley, and beyond the town, steepening as it rises, there is a green-brown lazy-looking mountain called Mickle. A few scattered farms occupy the lower slopes, and at one of these, Jones's Farm, it had been arranged that Gerald and Olive should leave some bills. A pony-cart drew up outside Uncle Richard's house soon after breakfast, and the journey began at a steady trot through street after street that Gerald had never been in before. The horse swished its tail from side to side, waving a red rosette tied on to it; big posters decorated the cart. The man who drove was called Fred. It was a lovely blue sunshiny morning, and when they had climbed a little way and looked back, they could see all Browd﹣ley flat below them, covered with a thin smoke﹣cloud, the factory chimneys sticking out of it like pins in a pincushion. Above them, very big now, the mountain lifted up. Gerald had never been close to a mountain before. He felt madly happy. The lane narrowed to a stony track where Fred had to get down several times to open gates. At last they reached the farm﹣house where Mrs. Jones lived. She was stand﹣ing at the doorway wiping her arms on an apron and smiling at them; she was very fat and had hair piled up on top of her head. When Gerald and Olive got down from the cart she hugged them. "Well . . . well . . . well . . ." she began, leading them inside the house; and just as they got into the kitchen a tabby cat suddenly moved from the hearthrug towards Gerald, tail erect. Gerald loved cats and stooped to stroke it, but he hadn't to stoop far, because (so the thought came to him) the cat was quite as large as a dog. Then he reflected that that wasn't a very sensible comparison, because dogs could be of all sizes, whereas cats had only one size, whatever size they were. Was that the way to put it? Anyway, Mrs. Jones's cat was a monster. It lifted up its head and met his hand in a warm, eager pressure that was beautiful to him. "Isn't she a big pussy?" said Mrs. Jones, standing with her fists at "hips firm," as they called it at Grayshott.

"She's a big cat," said Gerald gravely.

"Her name's Nib," continued Mrs. Jones, and began to say "Nibby, Nibby, Nibby," in a high-pitched voice. But the cat, after one shrewd upward glance, knew that this was all nonsense, and continued to heave up to Gerald's hand. While Gerald was thus entranced, Olive remembered the bills they had brought and handed them over. " Lawks-a-mussy," said Mrs. Jones, glancing at them, " it's Jones as'll read these, not me. A Liberal 'e is, that's very sure, even if it was his dyin' day."

Then she waddled away to a further room, the cat abruptly following her, and presently returned with pieces of cake, glasses, and a jug. " Nettle-drink," she said. The cat was purring loudly. " Sup it up—it'll do you good."

Gerald was looking at the mountain through the doorway. In the sunlight it looked as if it were moving towards him.

" Is it the highest mountain in England ?" he asked.

" Nay, that I can't say for certain—it'll happen not be as high as some on 'em."

" Isn't it the highest mountain of anywhere ?" asked Gerald desperately; but neither Mrs. Jones nor Fred seemed to understand. Fred said: " 'Tis only Mickle—I wouldn't call it much of a mountain at all."

93

All at once Gerald realised that it didn't matter how they answered : it *was* the highest mountain, the highest in the world, and he was going to climb it, like the men in the snow storm in his geography book.

He put down his glass and walked to the doorway. "I'm going up there," he said.

"Nay, you can't, you'd get lost on Mickle," said Mrs. Jones.

"But I want to see what's over the other side," Gerald went on.

"Take 'em both up, Fred, if they want," Mrs. Jones then said. "It'll be a bit o' fresh air for 'em."

Fred nodded and began to trudge slowly up the steep track, Gerald and Olive following. But after a little while Gerald scampered ahead, because he liked to think that nobody had ever climbed the mountain before. It was a dan gerous thing to do, and only he, the famous mountaineer and engine driver, dare risk it. Up, up, scrambling through bracken and heather; there were tigers, too, that you had to watch out for. His blood was racing as he reached the smooth green summit. The earth was at his feet, the whole earth, and over the other side, which he had been so curious about, a further mountain was to be seen—doubtless the second highest mountain in the world. Far below he could make out the tower of Browdley Church, with a tramcar crawling beside it like a red beetle.

Suddenly he saw a halfpenny lying on the ground. "Look what I've found!" he cried, triumphantly; then he lay down in the cool blue air and waited for the others to come up.

Fred smoked in silence while Gerald talked to Olive.

"What makes your father a Candidate?"

"Because there's an election."

"But what's that?"

"It means he has to get in."

"Where does he get in?"

"In the house."

"Can't anybody get in?"

"Only if you're a Candidate."

"Does he ever have a special train?"

"A special train? I—I don't know."

"Don't know what a special train is? Do you like trains? When I came here there was a Four-Four-Nought on our train. Bet you don't know what that means."

No answer.

"Are you afraid to touch a snail?"

"No. And I'm not afraid to touch a bee, either. Even a bumble-bee. I don't suppose you've ever seen a bumble-bee."

"Oh yes, I have. It's like a piece of flying cat. I wouldn't be afraid to touch one. But I'll bet you'd be afraid to stand on the edge of the platform while the Scotch express dashed through at sixty miles an hour. I did that once. I stood right on the edge."

"Why?"

"It was a test. None of the others could do

it. My father couldn't. Or Uncle Richard. Even the stationmaster couldn't."

"Why not ?"

"Because the train was going too fast. It was really going at eighty miles an hour, not sixty."

Then there was a long silence, while Gerald lay back staring at the sky. He was very, very happy.

When you are a child, everything you think and dream of has a piercing realness that never happens again ; there is no blurred background to that stereoscopic clarity, no dim perspective to drag at the heart's desire. That little world you live in is the widest, the loveliest, and the sweetest ; it can be the bitterest also.

To Gerald, alone in his own vivid privacy, everything seemed miraculously right except the Other Candidate, who was miraculously wrong. The warm red room with the brass rail over the fireplace, and the greenhouse with the tricycle in it, and the parrot who never forgave him and

whom he never forgave, were part of a secret
intimacy in which Uncle Richard and Olive
and Aunt Flo were partners (in descending order
of importance), and over which, only a little
lower than the angels, loomed the Candidate.
Gerald could never catch a glimpse of the
Candidate, though, after Uncle Richard's hint,
he always looked out for him on the stairs. He
knew that the Candidate lived in Uncle
Richard's house, working in the front parlour
with the door always closed, and sleeping in the
front bedroom over it; yet he could never (and
it must have been pure chance) see him entering
or leaving the house, or passing from one room
to another. Partly, of course, this was because
of Aunt Flo's continual fidgeting. "Mind
now, Gerald, be very quiet, and no playing in
the passage—the Candidate'll be in any minute." Or: "Gerald, time for bed now—must
have you out of the way before the Candidate
comes in !" Long after she had put him to
bed and turned out the light, Gerald would lie

awake, thinking and listening; often he *heard* the Candidate, but it was never any words— just the mix-up of footsteps and talk.   Once he said to Uncle Richard: "Can't I ever *see* the Candidate ?"—and Uncle Richard answered: "Not now, my boy—he's far too busy. But I'll take you out to-night and you'll see him then."

So that night Uncle Richard took Gerald to the market-place, which was full of a great crowd of people.   Uncle Richard hoisted him on to his shoulder so that he could see; and far away, over all the cloth caps, a man was standing on a cart and shouting something.   Gerald could not hear what it was he was shouting, because people round about were shouting much louder.   "Aha, we're in good time," said Uncle Richard, in Gerald's ear.   "That's only old Burstall—don't you take any notice of *him*. He'll only go on till the Candidate comes, that's all.   Watch out—you'll soon see the Candidate !"

The talking and shouting went on, and Gerald, perched on Uncle Richard's shoulder, began to feel very sleepy. Everyone seemed to be smoking pipes and cigarettes, and the smoke rose in a cloud and got into his eyes, so that it became hard to keep them open. The man on the cart continued to talk, but he wasn't interesting either to watch or listen to . . . and still the Candidate didn't come. . . . Then suddenly, with a jerk, Gerald felt himself being lowered to the ground and Uncle Richard was stooping and shaking him. All around were the legs of people hurrying past. "Why," exclaimed Uncle Richard, "I do believe you've been asleep ! Didn't you see the Candidate ?"

Then Gerald realised what had happened. Uncle Richard laughed heartily. "Well, I don't know—you are a rum fellow, and no mistake ! Badgering me all the time to see him, and then when he does come you drop off to sleep !"

"I couldn't help it," answered Gerald miserably. "I didn't know. . . . Why didn't you nudge me ?"

"Nudge you ? God bless my soul, I thought you were wide awake !" Uncle Richard went on laughing as if it were a great joke instead of something very sad. "Well, my boy, you missed something good, I can tell you. The Candidate's a treat—a fair treat !"

Days went by, and the chance did not come again. All the commotion of shouting and singing and waving red rosettes was reaching some kind of climax that Gerald, even without understanding it, could clearly sense ; every morning the magic was renewed, and Uncle Richard tapped the barometer with more zest for the day ahead.

In Gerald the desire to see the Candidate had grown into a great longing. It coloured all Browdley in a glow of excitement, for, as Uncle Richard had said : " You'll see him, my boy, if you keep your eyes open ! Ha, ha—if you keep

your eyes open, eh ? That hits the mark, eh ?
Wuff-wuff. . . . He's everywhere in Browdley
—you're bound to see him. But mind, now, no
hanging about the passage—that would only
annoy him. He's putting up a hard fight—
we've all got to help."

That was so, of course, and it was for that
reason he and Olive kept on putting bills in
letter-boxes. It was like Secret Service, where
you did things you didn't properly understand
because the King ordered you to ; though you
never really saw the King till afterwards, when
the danger was all past and he received you at
the Palace and conferred on you the Most
Noble and Distinguished Order of the Red
Rosette.

So Gerald wandered about, eager and happy
and preoccupied, full of thoughts of his mission
and stirred by wild hopes that some time, any
time, on the stairs or at the corner of the street,
the Candidate might suddenly appear. A
vision ! It was terribly exciting to think of—

quite the most exciting thing since Martin Secundus had measles and went to the sanatorium, and Gerald used to wait about outside thinking that Martin would probably die and would want to give him a last message from his death-bed.

One afternoon Gerald was alone in the house, reading the Yearly Report of the Browdley and District Friendly and Co-operative Society, which he had found under the cushion of a chair, and which seemed to him, for the moment, of engrossing interest. There was a picture in it of the first train entering Browdley station in 1853, and beside it, a picture of the first shop opened by the Browdley and District Friendly and Co-operative Society in the same year. A long, long time ago, before Uncle Richard was born. Gerald began to think about a long, long time ago, but it was hard to think like that. He was relieved when the tinkle of a bell in the street outside reminded him of his unique position—he was alone in the house, and the bell belonged to the ice-cream cart that visited the Parade every afternoon. Gerald had a passion for ice-cream, and one of his constant puzzle-ments was that grown-ups, who had pockets full of money and complete freedom to do any-thing they liked, didn't eat ice-cream all day long. Aunt Flo, for example, would nibble at a spoonful and say she " didn't care for it much —it's too cold " (what a ridiculous thing to say !) and Uncle Richard wouldn't have any at all. Profound mystery of human behaviour ! Some-times, however, they had allowed Gerald to go out into the street with a cup and buy a half-pennyworth. Now, with a sudden conscious-ness of his great chance, Gerald reached down from the dresser the largest cup he could find and took two pennies carefully out of his purse. Then he ran down the passage and out at the front-door. The ice-cream cart, drawn by a little donkey, stood in the middle of the road-way, with the ice-cream man sitting perched up inside it. It was a beautiful cart, covered with coloured pictures and gilt lettering, and with four bright brass pillars holding up a flat roof. It made the ice-cream man, whose name was Ulio, look like a king on his throne. " Two-pennyworth," said Gerald, a little nervously, lest Mr. Ulio should see into his inmost heart. But Mr. Ulio just jabbed at his ice-cream and scooped a few slices into the cup—and not very much more, Gerald thought, than he had formerly got for a halfpenny.

Gerald ran back into the house and began to eat the ice-cream in a great hurry, because it was " waste " when it melted, and it always did, towards the bottom of the cup. The parrot squawked and pattered up and down the bars of the cage ; she always demanded a share of any-thing that people were eating. Gerald, how-ever, took no notice of her, partly because of their long-standing feud, but chiefly because he would not have given away even a fraction of his ice-cream to anybody. While he was eating ice-cream he was transfixed with greed ; mind and body were united in the fulfilment of desire.

When the cup was empty he became his more usual self again; his passions became more mystical, more closely intertwined with thought. He was not sure what he would do next, but he ran into the greenhouse and stared for a time through the blue glass, which he liked better than the red. He was excitingly alone. The Candidate was out, Uncle Richard was out on his tricycle, Olive and Aunt Flo were "round the corner" on some errand. Suddenly a knock came at the front door and Gerald ran back to open it, hoping beyond hope that the Candidate might have returned unexpectedly and that he would say, when they had shaken hands: "Gerald, in all Browdley you are the man I have most of all been wanting to meet. I have heard of you, of course. Come into my parlour and let us talk. Has Mr. Ulio gone out of the street? I hope not, for I should like you to join me in a large dish of his excellent ice-cream.

. . ." But no; it was an ordinary man, just an ordinary man, wanting to see the Candidate. Gerald said he was out.

"Hasn't he come back yet? There's this letter for him. He's been up at the farms on Mickle this morning, so they say, but I reckoned he'd be back by now. Will you give him this letter when he comes?"

"Is it very important?"

"Oh, no, it'll do when he has a minute to spare. No particular hurry."

Gerald gave his promise, but as soon as the man was gone he came to the conclusion that the letter *was* very important, and that the man had only said it wasn't because it really was. Secret Service people did things like that. And since it was very important, and if the Candidate were still at the farms on Mickle, why should not Gerald go up there himself, immediately, and deliver it to the Candidate in person? They would meet, perhaps, in Mrs. Jones's kitchen. "Where is the young man who brought this message ? He has saved my life. *What ?* He lives with Uncle Richard ? And I never knew it !—How can I ever forgive my self ! . . . Mrs. Jones, bring us some of your nettle drink—we will all quaff together."

Gerald left the house, walked to the centre of the town, crossed the market place, and took the turning up the hill. The day was not so fine as when he had set out for Mickle before, and the mountain itself looked heavy and dark; but Gerald did not mind that—he had too many exciting thoughts. At one place where the street narrowed and two factories faced each other, he imagined that the walls were leaning over, and that if he didn't hurry they would fall on him. So he broke into a scamper till the danger was past, and then stood panting and not quite sure whether he was really afraid or only pretending. Then he took the Candidate's letter out of his pocket and looked at it solemnly; it reminded him of what he had to do. He hurried on. Presently he came to the end of the houses; the lane twisted and became steeper; a few drops of rain fell. He thought of the warm red room at Uncle Richard's with Aunt Flo making potato-cakes as she probably would be by this time, and just beginning to wonder where he was; the clatter of cups and the kettle singing, the parrot squawking for a spoonful of tea. Would it not be safer to go back? But no; no; he must climb up and up and deliver the letter to the Candidate. He came to a line of high trees; if there were an odd number of them, perhaps he would go back, but if there were an even number he would keep on. There were twelve. He often settled difficult problems by this kind of method, though he never told anybody about it, except Martin Secundus, who understood. He began to walk faster uphill. You cannot do it, they all cried, mocking him as he passed by; it is too dangerous to climb this mountain; no one has ever done it and come back alive. It is my duty, he answered proudly, as he swept on.

Then he began to see that the sky was dark-ening, not with rain only, but with twilight; the top of Mickle lay in a little cloud, as if some-one had drawn the outline of the mountain in ink and then smudged it. He felt tired and his legs trembled. Soon the rain began to fall faster, until there was no mountain to see at all —only a grey curtain covering it; but he knew he was on the right path, because of the steep-ness. Never, remarked the famous engine-driver, do I remember such a night of wind and rain. . . .

He walked on and on, climbing all the time, till the rain had soaked through all his clothes, and was clammy-cold against his skin.

Suddenly he heard a noise, a strange noise, a kind of rumbling and muttering from the road ahead. He stopped, scared a little, listening to it above the swishing of the rain and the whine of the wind in the telegraph-wires. The noise grew louder, and all at once two bright yellow lights poked round a corner and came rushing at him. He ran for safety to the side of the road, and there slipped on some mud and fell. The next he knew was that the rumbling noise had halted somehow beside him, and had changed and lowered its key. Someone was holding him up and feeling his arms.

"No bones broken, Roberts. I'm sure we didn't touch him—he just slipped and fell over. We'd best take him along with us, anyhow."

"Yes, sir."

Gerald found himself lifted off his feet with his face pressing against something rain-drenched and fluffy. A ray of yellow light caught it, and he saw then that it was a rosette fastened to a man's overcoat.

A blue rosette.

Blue.

Once again the truth besieged him in an over-powering rush. This man who was holding him must be the Other Candidate . . . and the noise-making Thing near by must be the motor-car. There could be no doubt about it.

III

And he was shaken. He felt fear, horror, and the simple presence of evil. "Let me go!" he shouted desperately, wriggling and twisting and hitting the man's face with his fists.

"Here, what's the matter, youngster?"

"Let me go—let me go!"

"What's all the fuss about? You aren't hurt, are you? Better get him in the car, Roberts."

"No! No, no!"

"Well, what the devil *do* you want?"

Now that the man had used a swear, like that, Gerald was more certain than ever that he must be the Other Candidate. And knowing that he was the Other Candidate, it was easy to see what a wicked face he had. Terrible eyes and a curving nose and a sneery mouth, like pictures of pirates. And what he wanted to do, undoubtedly, was to steal the Candidate's letter that Gerald was carrying. Gerald looked around wildly. The man had put him down to earth again, that was something; but both the men seemed so huge above him, and the falling rain seemed to enclose the darkness through which lay his only chance of escape.

"Come on," said the man roughly. "This is no place to hang about all night. We'd better make sure and take him along with us, Roberts."

"Very good, sir."

"No!" screamed Gerald. "You carpet-bagger!" And with that and a quick bound into the middle of the darkness, he ran down the hill, leaving the two men standing by the motor-car. He heard them laughing; then he heard them shouting after him and to each other; then he heard them beginning to run after him. He plunged sideways into a hedge, scratching his face and arms and bruising his eye against a thick branch. At last he managed to struggle through the long wet grasses of a field. He could hear the two men running down the hill; they passed within a few yards of him on the other side of the hedge; they passed by. As soon as he had gained breath he began to stumble farther across the field. They should not take him alive, and they should not find the Candidate's letter. So he tore it up into very little pieces and let go a few of them whenever there came a big gust of wind. When they were all gone he felt brave again and wished he had some other papers to tear up and throw away.

It was ten o'clock at night when Gerald, in charge of a policeman, arrived at Number 2, The Parade. The Candidate was out, but Uncle Richard and Aunt Flo were waiting up, worried and anxious and by no means reassured by Gerald's first appearance. For he was nearly speechless with exhaustion; his clothes were drenched and mud-plastered; his arms and face were streaked with scratches, and he had an unmistakable black eye. All the policeman could say was that he had found him fast asleep in a shop-doorway along the Mickle road, and that he had been incapable of giving any account of what had happened to him—only the fact that he lived at Number 2, The Parade.

Uncle Richard fetched the doctor; meanwhile Aunt Flo rubbed Gerald with towels, gave him some Benger's Food, and put him to bed with three hot bricks wrapped round with pieces of blanket. He was fast asleep again long before the doctor came.

In the morning he felt much better except for a certain dazedness, aches in most of his limbs, and an eye which he could hardly open. Uncle Richard and Aunt Flo were beside his bed when he woke up. He smiled at them, because they were Good, and he was Good, and Uncle Richard's house was a Good House. They began to ask him what had happened, and when he was awake enough he launched into the full story of how he had been walking along the road when suddenly . . .

" What road ? "

" The road to Mrs. Jones' Farm."

" Jones' Farm !" shouted Aunt Flo, repeating the words in a loud voice so that Uncle Richard, who was deafer than usual some mornings, could hear. " But what on earth were you doing along that road ? "

Gerald dared not mention the letter to the Candidate, because it was a Secret Document, and Secret Documents were not to be divulged even to one's best friends. So he said, in a casual way which he hoped would sound convincing : " I wanted to see Mrs. Jones and Nibby."

" Nibby ? "

" The cat. A very big cat." He remembered with disfavour how Mrs. Jones had called it " a big pussy."

" Mrs. Jones and her cat ! " shouted Aunt Flo. " He says he was going to see Mrs. Jones and her cat ! The Mrs. Jones at Jones' Farm ! Did you ever hear such a story ! "

" Wuff-wuff," said Uncle Richard.

" Go on," said Aunt Flo, warningly. "And let's have the whole truth, mind. We know you bought some ice-cream off Ulio's cart when he came round in the afternoon, because Mrs. Silberthwaite saw you."

Gerald did not know who Mrs. Silberthwaite was, but he felt that it had been none of her business, anyhow. He went on, reproachfully : "You see, a motor-car came down the hill."

"A motor-car !" shouted Aunt Flo, in great excitement. "Richard, listen to that ! He says a motor-car met him along the road ! It would be Beale's motor-car, for certain—there's only the one ! Beale in his motor-car knocked him down !"

Now this was not what Gerald had said at all, but he thought it an interesting variant of what had really happened, and he was just picturing it in his mind when Uncle Richard let out one of his biggest and most emphatic "wuffs."

"God bless my soul, that young carpet-bagger knocked him down ! Knocked the boy down with his new-fangled stinking contraption ! Knocked the boy down—God bless

117

my soul ! We'll have the law on him, *that* we will—it'll cost him something—wuff-wuff—knocked the boy down in the public highway ! Goodness gracious, the Candidate must know immediately ! Wuff—immediately ! When Browdley hears of all this, young Beale won't stand a chance ! It'll turn the election—mark my words——"

And Uncle Richard began capering out of the room and down the stairs with more agility than Gerald had ever seen him employ before. Gerald was excited. His mind was racing to catch the flying threads of a hundred possibilities; meanwhile Aunt Flo was rushing about to "tidy up" the room; for the Candidate was like the Doctor in this, that it would never do to let him catch sight of a crooked picture or a hole in the counterpane.

After a few moments footsteps climbed the stairs, slowly and creakingly; Uncle Richard was talking loudly; another voice, rather tired and hoarse, was answering.

And so, after those many wonderful days of waiting and dreaming, Gerald at last met the Candidate face to face; and because he knew he was the Candidate he saw what a kind and beautiful face it was, the face of a real knight. Overwhelmed with many thoughts, transfigured with worship, Gerald smiled, and the Candidate smiled back and touched the boy's forehead. Gerald thrilled to that touch as he had never thrilled to anything before, not even when he had first seen the Bassett-Lowke shop in London.

"Better now?" asked the Candidate.

Gerald slowly nodded. He could not speak for a moment, he was so happy; it was so marvellously what he had longed for, to have the Candidate talking to him kindly like that.

"Tell the gentleman what happened," said Aunt Flo, on guard at the foot of the bed.

"Yes, do, please," said the Candidate, still with that gentle, comforting smile.

"I will," answered Gerald, gulping hard or

he would have begun to cry. And he added, in a whisper : " Sir Thomas."

They all smiled at that ; which was odd, Gerald thought, for there could really be no joke in calling the Candidate by his proper name. He went on : " You see, the motor-car came straight at me——"

" He says the motor-car charged straight into him !" shouted Aunt Flo, for Uncle Richard's benefit.

" Let the boy tell his own story," said the Candidate.

That calmed them, and also, in a queer way, it gave Gerald calmness of his own. He continued : " The motor-car came charging into me and knocked me over——"

" Was it going fast ?"

" It was going *very* fast," answered Gerald, and added raptly : " Nearly as fast as the Scotch Express."

" He's all trains," said Aunt Flo. " Never thinks of anything else."

But the Candidate showed an increasing un-willingness to listen to her. "So the motor-car was travelling fast," he said to Gerald quietly, "and I suppose you were knocked down because you couldn't get away in time. Is that it ?"

"Yes, sir—Sir Thomas."

"And what happened then ?"

"The motor-car stopped and two men got out and came up to me. One of them was wearing a blue badge."

"Beale !" cried Aunt Flo. "Didn't I say so ? Richard, he says one of them was Beale himself !"

"Please go on," said the Candidate.

Gerald said after a pause : "They picked me up and stared at me."

"Stared at you ?"

"Yes. That's what they did."

"And what after that ?"

What, indeed ? Gerald could not, for the moment, remember just how everything had happened. But suddenly the answer came. "They laughed," he said.

"They *what* ?" asked the Candidate, leaning forward nearer to Gerald.

"He says they jeered at him !" shouted Aunt Flo.

"They laughed," continued Gerald, with gathering confidence. "And one of them said it was all my fault for being in the way. He hit me." Pause. "He hit me in the eye. I ran away then and they both chased me, but they couldn't catch me." He sighed proudly. "I ran too fast."

"Richard—Richard—just listen to that— would you believe it—he says they hit him !"

"Wuff-wuff—my goodness—wuff—just wait —scandalous—wuff——"

"Tell me now," said the Candidate, still quietly. "You say one of the men hit you and gave you this black eye. You're sure he hit you ?"

"He hit me," answered Gerald, with equal quietness, "*twice*."

Gerald stayed in bed for several days after that, for it seemed that despite all the doctoring and hot bricks, he was destined to catch the thoroughly bad cold that he deserved. For a time his temperature was high—high enough to swing the hours along in an eager, throbbing trance, invaded by consciousness of strange things happening in the rooms below and in the streets outside. Voices and footsteps grew noisier and more continual, shouting and singing waved distantly over the roof-tops. Aunt Flo brought him jellies and beef-tea, and Uncle Richard sometimes came up for a cheery word; but for the most part Gerald was left alone, while the rest of the house abandoned itself to some climax of activity. He could feel all that, as he lay huddled up under the bedclothes. But he was not unhappy to be left alone, because he felt the friendliness of the house like a warm animal all around him, something alive and breathing and lovely to be near. There had been nothing in his life like this before. He could not remember his father and mother (they had both died when he was a baby); and Aunt Lavinia, who usually took charge of him during the school holidays, lived in a dull, big house in a dull, small place where nothing ever happened—nothing, at any rate, like this magic of Browdley streets and Ulio's ice-cream and climbing right to the very top of Mickle.

But the most wonderful thing of all had been when the Candidate bent over him and touched his forehead. As he lay feverishly in bed and thought of it, it all happened over again, but with more detail—with every possible detail.

"Gerald Holloway, I owe everything to you. If that letter had been discovered. . . ." And suddenly Gerald thought of a big improvement: the Candidate was really his father, who hadn't actually died but had somehow got lost, but now here he was, found again, and they

124

were both going to be together for always. They would live in the Parade, quite near to Uncle Richard, and Gerald need never go back to Grayshott except to see Martin Secundus and ask him to come and stay with them. "Father . . . this is Martin . . ."

And when he grew up he would go on serving his father in the Secret Service, because he was more than an ordinary father. He was a Loving Father, like the Father people talked about in church.

The clock on the mantelpiece ticked through Gerald's dreaming, ticking on the seconds to the time when he should be grown up and a man. What a long time ahead, but it was passing; he was eight already, and he could remember as far back as when he was four and Aunt Lavinia hit him for blowing on his rice pudding to make it cold.

But why "*Our* Father"? *My* Father, he said to himself proudly, remembering how the Candidate had smiled.

So the hours passed in that shabby little back bedroom at Uncle Richard's; but Gerald never noticed the shabbiness, never noticed that the furniture was cheap and the wallpaper faded, never realised from such things that Uncle Richard and Aunt Flo were poor people compared with rich Aunt Lavinia in her dull, big house. All he felt was the realness here, and the unrealness of everywhere else in the world.

One morning the Doctor pronounced him better and fit to get up. "His school begins again on Tuesday," said Aunt Flo. "Will he be able to go?"

"Good gracious, yes," replied the Doctor. "Good gracious, yes."

Till then Gerald had had hopes that somehow the cloud of Grayshott on the horizon might be lifted, that the holidays would not end as all other holidays had done; but now, hearing that most clinching "Good gracious, yes," he felt a pin-point of misery somewhere inside the middle of him, and it grew and grew with every minute of thinking about it.

That night was very quiet and there were no footsteps or voices, and in the morning, when he got up and dressed and went downstairs, he saw that the door of the parlour was wide open.

"Well," said Uncle Richard, tapping the barometer as usual, "so here you are again, young shaver."

There was a difference somewhere. Something had happened. After breakfast he began to ask, as he had so often begun: "Can Olive and I——" and Uncle Richard said: "Eh, what's that? Olive's not here any more— wuff-wuff—she's gone away with her father."

"Gone away? The Candidate's gone away?"

Uncle Richard laughed loudly. "Don't you go calling him the Candidate any more, my boy. Because he isn't. He's the Member now."

"What's the Member?"

"It means he's Got In. Margin of twenty-three—narrow squeak—but that doesn't matter. Still, it shows he wouldn't have done but for young Beale's behaviour with that motor-car of his—perfectly scandalous thing—as I said at the time — perfectly scandalous — wuff-wuff — and consequently was—as I said—it turned the scale. Turned the scale—wuff-wuff—didn't I say it would ?"

All this was nothing that Gerald could understand much about, except that the Candidate had gone. "Uncle Richard," he said slowly, and then paused. Aunt Flo shouted: "Richard, why don't you answer the boy ? He wants to ask you something !"

Uncle Richard put his hand to his ear. "Ask away, my boy."

"Uncle Richard—will it—all—ever—happen—again ?"

"Eh, what ? Happen again ? Will what happen again ?"

Then Gerald knew it was no use ; even Uncle

Richard couldn't understand. He ran away into the greenhouse and stared through the red glass.

The next morning Aunt Flo wakened him early and gave him a brown egg for breakfast, because he had "a journey in front of him." Then he kissed her and said good-bye, and looked at the tricycle in the greenhouse for the last time. Uncle Richard took him to the station and told the guard about his luggage and where he was going. Thump, thump, thump, along the wooden platform; the train came in, actually drawn by a Four-Six-Nought, but Gerald had hardly the heart to notice it.

"Good-bye, my boy. Wuff-wuff. Don't forget to change at Crewe—the guard will put you right. And here you are—this is to buy yourself some sweets when you get back to school."

Fancy, thought Gerald, Uncle Richard didn't know that you weren't allowed to buy sweets at school; still, a shilling would be useful;

perhaps he would buy some picture-postcards of railway engines. "Oh, thank you, Uncle Richard. . . . Good-bye . . . Good-bye."

"Good-bye, my boy."

Gerald kept his head out of the window and waved his hand till the train curved out of sight of the station. Then, as the wheels gathered speed, they began to say things. . . . Grayshott to-night, Grayshott to-night. . . . This time a week ago. . . . This time two weeks ago. . . . Oh dear, how sad that was. . . . The train entered a tunnel and Gerald decided: If I can hold my breath until the end of this tunnel, then it means that I shall soon go to Uncle Richard's again and the Candidate will be there and Olive too, and we shall all climb Mickle together and see Mrs. Jones and Nibby. . . . He held his breath till he felt his ears singing and his eyes pricking . . . then he had to give way while the train was still in the tunnel. That was an awful thing to have had to do. He took out of his pocket the pencil he had poked Polly with (that first morning, how far away!) and began to write his name on the cardboard notice that forbade you to throw bottles on the line. "Gerald," he wrote; but then, more urgently, it occurred to him to black out the "p" in "Spit," so that it read "Please do not Sit." Very funny, that was; he must tell Martin Secundus about that, because Martin had his own train-joke when there was nobody else in the compartment; he used to cross out the "s" in "To Seat Five," so that it read "To Eat Five." Gerald did not think this was quite as funny as "Please do not Sit." But suddenly in the midst of thinking about it, a wave of misery came over him at having to leave Uncle Richard's, and he threw himself into a corner seat and hid his face in the cushions.

All this happened a long time ago. Gerald never stayed with Uncle Richard again.

Uncle Richard is dead, but Aunt Flo is still living, an old woman, in a small cottage on the outskirts of Browdley—for Number 2, The Parade, has been pulled down to make room for Browdley's biggest super-cinema. The parrot, too, still lives—as parrots will. Just the two of them, in that small cottage.

The Candidate is dead, and Olive is married —to somebody in India, not such a good match, folks say.

The Other Candidate, however, has done pretty well for himself, as you would realise if you heard his name. He is in Parliament, of course, but not as member for Browdley. Indeed, if he ever thinks of Browdley, it is with some natural distaste for a town whose slanderous gossip circulated the most fantastic stories about him once, delaying his career, he reckons, by three whole years. He is very popular and a fine after-dinner speaker.

And Gerald grew up to be happy and miserable like any other boy. He passed from Grayshott to Brookfield, where he became head of Chips's house ; then he went to Cambridge and took a double-first.   But it is true to say that the world was never more wonderful to him than during that holiday at Uncle Richard's when he was eight, and never afterwards was he as miserable (not even during the War) as in the train going back to Grayshott; never did he adore anyone quite so purely as he adored the Candidate, or hate so fiercely as he hated the Other Candidate.

And never afterwards did he tell such a down-right thumping lie, nor was there a time ever again when right and wrong seemed to him so simply on this side and on that.   A little boy then, and a man now if he had lived; he was killed on July 1st, 1916. When Chips read out his name in Brookfield Chapel that week, his voice broke and he could not go on.

3

YOUNG
WAVENEY

3

WHEN Waveney had been at Brookfield for a month he was moved up
into the Lower Fourth, Mr. Pear-
son's form; which was a pity, because he did
not like Mr. Pearson. Nor, to be quite frank,
did Mr. Pearson like *him*. For Waveney was
everything that Mr. Pearson was not; he was
young, he was attractive, and he possessed an
inexhaustible vitality. Mr. Pearson, on the other
hand, was no longer young; he had never been
particularly attractive, and he had lately become

137

exceedingly tired. Actually he was forty-three, and owing to a weak heart that made him ineligible for the Army, he had come to Brookfield as a war-time deputy.

How a schoolmaster must envy a boy who is obviously going to grow up into a man of much superior personality to his own, and how easily that envy can turn to loathing if the boy senses it and is cruel !

Waveney was not cruel, but he was a passionate hater of injustice, and before he had been in Mr. Pearson's class for a week, that passionate hatred was aroused.

For Mr. Pearson had a *system*. The system, which had served well enough at his previous school, was new to Brookfield; and it was as follows. If anyone in his class talked or fooled about while his back was turned, Mr. Pearson would swing round to try to catch him, but if (being rather short-sighted) he failed to do so, he would say: "Stand up the boy who did that." Nobody would respond, of course, because there was a feeling at Brookfield that a school-master had no *right* to ask such a question. He ought to spot offenders for himself, or else leave them unspotted. For after all, as young Waveney eloquently remarked, if you ride your bicycle on the footpath, you may be copped, but you aren't expected to go to the police-station and give yourself up; and all life was rather like that, one way and another.

Wherefore it was manifestly unjust for Mr. Pearson, when nobody made a confession, to pull out a large gunmetal watch, hold it dramatically in one hand, and say: " Very well, if the boy who did it doesn't own up within twenty seconds, I shall detain the whole form for half an hour after morning school. . . . Five . . . Ten . . . Fifteen . . . Very well, then, you will all meet me here again at twelve-thirty."

Partly by its detestable novelty, the system worked after a few preliminary trials, and Mr. Pearson's class remained fairly free from ragging.

Which, doubtless, may be held to justify the
system; for Mr. Pearson knew from long
experience that, in matters of class discipline, he
was such stuff as screams are made of.

Now young Waveney, who was about as
clever as an eleven-year-old can well be without
achieving something absolutely insufferable, had
declared war on Mr. Pearson right from the first
day, when in answer to a question in a history
test-paper: "What do you know about the Star
Chamber?"—he had written: "Nothing";
and had afterwards claimed full marks, because,
as he said, it was a perfectly correct answer.
"It wasn't *my* fault, sir, that you framed the
question badly—what you *meant* to say, sir, was
' *Write* what you know about the Star Chamber '—we like to be accurate about these things
at Brookfield, you know, sir." Mr. Pearson did
not give him full marks, but he mentally
catalogued him as a boy to beware of; and
Waveney mentally catalogued *him* as a poor sort
of fish, anyway.

" The system," however, brought matters to a head. As Waveney urged afterwards to an excited mass-meeting of fourth-formers— " Can't you see that the whole thing's just beastly unfair on everybody ? He can't keep order himself, and he expects us to do the job for him. If we don't own up, we're supposed to be letting other people down—sort of honour-bright business—pretty convenient for him, when you come to think about it. Well, any-how, I warn you, I'm going to make a stand, and I advise all you others to do the same. In future, let's arrange not to own up—ever— when he tries his little game. Let him spot us himself, if he wants to—why should we save him trouble ? And if he keeps us in after hours, then let's all put up with it for a time until he gets tired. He soon will. Mind now, not another confession from anybody—we'll soon break his rotten system ! "

As it happened, Waveney was himself the first to make the experiment. On the following day, he threw a piece of inky paper while Mr. Pearson's back was turned, refused to confess himself the thrower when the gunmetal watch was brought out, and became thus the cause of a detention for the whole class. The detention took place, and at the end of it Mr. Pearson said: " Some coward among you has allowed you all to suffer rather than confess his own trivial misdeed. I will give him another chance to declare himself, failing which I shall have no alternative but to repeat this detention every day until Conscience has done its work."

Afterwards, in rising fury, Waveney told his companions: " Well, if *that's* his game, we'll see who can stick it out the longest ! Only, mind, you fellows have got to back me up ! It's hard luck on you for the time being, but I'm breaking the system for you, don't forget that ! "

Another detention followed on the next day, and another after that. Young Waveney became more and more tight-lipped about it ; he was certainly not enjoying himself, though he was sustained by the feeling that he was leading a moral crusade. After the third detention Mr. Pearson said: "I am truly sorry for the hardship that some unspeakable coward is in- flicting on you all, and if you should happen to know who he is, I don't for a moment suggest that you should tell me, but I have no doubt that you will let *him* know—in your own way— what you think of his behaviour." It became disappointingly clear, moreover, that Mr. Pear- son did not greatly mind the detentions; he read a novel all the time, and as he was a lonely man with few social engagements an extra half-hour a day did not much matter to him.

Unfortunately the fourth form had many social engagements—in particular the annual match against Barnhurst, of which one of the detentions compelled them to miss the be- ginning. Ladbroke, a keen cricketer (which Waveney was not), said, rather curtly: "Pity you chose this week of all weeks for your stunt, Waveney."

After the fourth detention someone said: "Waveney daren't own up now, he's in too much of a funk—so I suppose we'll all get kept in for ever."

After the fifth detention Waveney found himself suddenly unpopular, and he hated it. "Bit of a swine, young Waveney, the way he's carrying on—pity he hasn't got more guts, he'd have owned up long since. Pearson says it's a cowardly thing to do, and I reckon it is, too."

After the sixth detention Waveney went to Mr. Pearson in his room and confessed.

"Ah," said Mr. Pearson, who was not essentially an unkind man (especially when his enemy was humbled), "so you are the culprit, eh?"

"Yes."

"And it is for you that your classmates have already suffered so much—and so undeservedly?"

"Yes, I did it."

"And you found you could not go on, eh?

The pangs of Conscience became too acute—
the still, small voice that spoke inside you,
telling you it was a mean thing to have done, a
cowardly thing—isn't that what it told you,
Waveney—isn't that why the tears are in your
eyes ?"

"No," answered Waveney, nearly howling
with rage. "I think it's nothing but a
dirty trap, and it's your rotten system that's
really the mean and cowardly thing, and—
and——"

Mr. Pearson faced Waveney with a glassy
stare. His moment was spoilt. "Waveney,
you forget yourself! And you will go to the
Headmaster for being intolerably impudent—
impudence, sir, is a thing I will *not* put up
with. . . ."

So young Waveney was summoned to
Chips's study that same evening. Chips was
seventy then, recalled from a well-earned retirement to assume the temporary headship of
Brookfield during the War years. He had

been at Brookfield for nearly half a century, and he had known boys rather like young Waveney before. He had also known masters rather like Mr. Pearson before. There was not much, indeed, that Chips had not known before; only the details, the patterned configurations of events, were apt to rearrange themselves.

"Well—umph?" he said, peering over his spectacles across the desk and giving his characteristic chuckle.

"Mr. Pearson sent me, sir."

"Umph—yes—you're Waveney, yes—umph —Mr. Pearson sent me a little note about you. Some little—umph — misunderstanding — eh? Suppose you—umph—tell me about it—in your own words?"

Waveney launched into a concise account of exactly what had happened (he was really a very clear-minded boy), while Chips listened with an occasional twitching of the eyes and face. When the tale was told, Chips sat for a moment in silence, looking at Waveney. At length he

said : " Bless me, boy, what a chatterer you are—
you take after your father—umph—he was pre-
sident of the debating society—talked the biggest
—umph—nonsense—I ever heard ! And now
he's—umph—in Parliament—well, well, I'm
not surprised. . . ."

After a pause he went on :

" But you know, Waveney—umph—you're
not fair to Mr. Pearson. You'd make his life a
misery—umph—if you could—and you blame
him because—umph—he's found a way of
stopping you ! Come, come—he's got to
protect himself against all you fourth-form
ruffians—umph—eh ? "

" But it's the system, sir."

" Systems, my boy, are hard things to fight. I
warn you of that. . . . Well, I must do something with you—umph—I suppose. What do
you—umph—suggest ? "

" I—I don't know, sir."

" The—umph—usual ? "

" If you like, sir."

147

"Umph—as if *I* care—so long as *you're* satisfied—umph . . . but there's one thing, Waveney . . ."

"Yes, sir?"

"Be—be *kind*, my boy."

"*Kind*, sir?"

"Yes—umph—even when you're fighting systems. Because there are—umph—human beings—behind those systems. . . . And now —umph—run along."

Chips watched the boy's receding figure as he walked to the door across the study carpet; then, with a half-smile to himself, he called out: "Oh, Waveney——"

"Yes, sir?"

"What—umph—are you going to be when you grow up?"

"I don't know, sir."

"Well—umph—I think I can tell you. You're going to be either—umph—a great man or—umph—a confounded nuisance. . . . Or —umph—both . . . as so many of 'em are.

. . . Remember that. . . . Good-bye, my boy. . . ."

After Waveney had gone, Chips sat for a time at his desk, thinking about the boy; then he wrote a note asking Mr. Pearson to come and see him.

4

MR·CHIPS
TAKES A RISK

4

IT is the wise man who is often wise enough not to know too much, and in his eighty-second year Mr. Chips had grown to be very wise indeed. Living in peaceful retirement after more than half a century of school-mastering, it was possible for him to enter his old school well aware that, in mere items of knowledge, most Brookfield boys could teach him quite as much as they could learn from him. "What *is* a straight eight?" he might ask, innocently, and when a dozen young voices had

153

finished explaining, he would reply, with the characteristic chuckle that everyone at Brookfield had imitated for years: "Umph—umph—I see. I just wondered how an eight—umph—could possibly be straight—umph—that was all. I thought perhaps—umph—Mr. Einstein had changed—umph—even the shape of the figures. . . ."

He was always apt to joke about mathematics, partly because (as he freely confessed) he had never understood "all this—umph—$x^2 + y^2$ business." Nor, with such an attitude, was it surprising that he regarded High Finance with something of the bewilderment (but none of the adoration) with which a South Sea Islander regards a sewing-machine. Indeed he once said: "Few people understand High Finance, and—umph—the higher it goes, the fewer!" He was certainly not of the few, and whenever he had any small capital to invest he put it prudently, if unadventurously, into British Government securities. Only once did he stray from this orthodox path, and that was when (on the advice of a new and excessively plausible bank manager) he bought a few shares in National and International Trust Limited, a corporation which, in the early spring of 1929, seemed as reliable as its name.

One April morning of that year Chips found the following letter on his breakfast‑table:

"DEAR OLD CHIPS,—Just to remind you that we don't seem to have met for years. Do you remember me ? You once thrashed me for climbing on the roof of the Big Hall—that was way back in 1903, which is a long time ago. If you are ever in town nowadays, do please have lunch with me at the St. Swithin's Club. I should enjoy a chat over old times.

Yours ever,
CHARLES E. MENVERS."

Which was just the sort of letter from an Old Brookfield boy that Chips delighted to receive.

He replied that very morning, in his neat and very minute handwriting:

"Dear Menvers,—Of course I remember you, and you will doubtless be glad to know that your roof exploit still holds the Brookfield record for impudence and foolhardiness. I happen to be visiting London next Thursday, so I will lunch with you then with pleasure. . . ."

So it came about that Mr. Chips entered the luxurious precincts of the St. Swithin's Club for the first time in his life and was welcomed by a handsome, fresh-complexioned man of middle-age, who had once been a boy with keen eyes and a mischievous face. The eyes were still keen, and to Chips it even seemed that the look of mischief had not disappeared entirely.

"Hullo, Chips! Fine to see you again. You don't look a day older!"

They all said that. Chips answered: "I can't—umph—return the compliment. You look *many* days older!"

Menvers laughed and took the old man's arm affectionately as they entered the famous St. Swithin's dining-room.

"Never been here before, Chips? Ah, well, I don't suppose business often takes you into the City. This is the Cathedral of High Finance, y'know. Why, I reckon there are a dozen millionaires having lunch in this room at the present moment. . . . And I'm one of 'em. Did you know *that*?"

No, Chips hadn't known that. "I'm afraid —umph—I never had much of a head for figures."

Menvers laughed again. There was nothing of the conventional caricatured financier about him. He was not fat, bloated, or truculent in manner. He did not wear a heavy gold watch-chain—merely an inconspicuous silver wrist-watch. And he did not smoke cigars— just ordinary cigarettes. Except for a veneer of self-display that was more flamboyant than really boastful, he had still the boyish charm that Chips so well remembered. And also (as he proudly confided) he had a pretty wife and one child, a boy. "Hope to put him into Brookfield in September, Chips. Keep an eye on him, won't you?"

Chips reminded him that he had long retired from schoolmastering and took no active part in the life of the modern Brookfield, but Menvers brushed the implication aside. "Nonsense, Chips. My spies report that your footsteps are heard on dark nights pacing up and down the old familiar corridors. . . . What was that tag in Virgil you used to teach us—begins ' *Quadrupedante putrem* '—ah yes, I remember now— ' *Quadrupedante putrem sonitu quatit ungula campum*.' Have I got it right?"

"Perfectly right," answered Chips, "except that—umph—I am not yet—umph—a ghost, and I was never—umph—a horse. . . . But I'm glad to find you still keep up your classical knowledge. It was never—umph—so considerable as to be—umph—a burden to you."

158

So they talked and joked together throughout a simple but exquisitely expensive meal. Chips found that he still liked Menvers, and neither more nor less because the fellow was a millionaire. Nor, in his innocence, did it occur to him as in the least remarkable that a wealthy City magnate should devote two hours of a busy day to reminiscing with an octogenarian schoolmaster. Finally, when they were on the point of shaking hands and wishing each other the best of luck, Menvers said:

"Oh, by the way, Chips, I happen to be on the board of National and International Trust, and I saw your name on our register the other day. . . . Hardly the sort of investment for *you*, I should have thought. Quite safe, mind you—don't think there's anything wrong about it. But what's the matter with War Loan for a staid old buffer like yourself?"

Chips explained about his bank manager's recommendation, to which Menvers listened with, it seemed, a touch of exasperation.

" Those fellows shouldn't take chances—why can't they leave that sort of thing to those in the game ? . . . Not, mind you, that I want to give you a false impression. The stock's sound enough. . . . Fact is, I want as much of it for myself as I can get hold of. What did you pay for your packet ? "

And Chips, of course, having no head for figures, couldn't remember. But by the time he reached his house at Brookfield that evening a long and (he thought) a quite unnecessarily costly telegram awaited him. It ran:

AFTER YOUR DEPARTURE I FOUND OUT PRICE YOU PAID FOR NATS AND INTERNATS STOP OFFER YOU DOUBLE IF YOU WILL SELL STOP BEG YOU TO DO SO AND DEVOTE PROFIT IF YOU WISH TO SCHOOL MISSION OR ANY SIMILAR RACKET REGARDS CHARLES THE ROOFWALKER.

Now Chips, had he been a shrewd thinker in financial matters, would have argued: This man wants my stock so urgently that he is apparently willing to pay twice the market price for it. Ergo, since he is a financier and in the know, there must be something especially promising about it, and I should do better to refuse his offer and hold on. But Chips was not a shrewd thinker of this kind. He was simple enough to feel that acceptance of the offer was an easy way of obliging Menvers and at the same time benefiting a deserving charity. So he wrote (not telegraphed) an acceptance; and that was that.

April, remember. In June, as you probably won't need to remember, National and International Trust crashed into spectacular bankruptcy. When Chips saw the newspaper headlines his immediate reaction made him write to Menvers a sympathetic note in which he said :

"I feel that your generous purchase of my shares was so recent that I cannot possibly allow you to bear any extra loss, however small, that would otherwise have fallen on me. I am therefore enclosing my cheque for the full amount. . . ."

By return came a scribbled postcard enclosed in an envelope :

"I have torn up your cheque. Don't be a damned fool. I could see this coming and I wanted to get you out in time. If you must help me, pray for me. . . ."

Two days later the arrest of Charles E. Menvers on serious and complicated charges of fraud provided the City with its biggest sensation for years.

Chips, as I have stressed all along, did not understand High Finance. His business code, so far as he had any, was simple—to sell things fairly (though in point of fact he never sold anything in his life except old books to a second-hand dealer), to pay all debts promptly (which was easy for him, as he never owed anything but gas and lighting bills), and to give generously to the needy (which was also easy for him, as he was in the habit of living well within his income). Simple—yes, simple as his life. He didn't understand the money axis on which the lives of so many people revolve—or stop revolving. What he *did* understand, however, was the notion that any one of his old boys never ceased to be *his*, no matter what happened . . . no matter *what* happened . . . and therefore, though he was old enough to find such a duty arduous, he attended every session of the four-day trial of Charles Menvers.

He sat for hours in one of the back rows of the public gallery at the Old Bailey, listening to expositions by counsel, long arguments by accounting experts, judicial rulings on incomprehensible issues, and (the only really interesting interludes) the prisoner's evidence under cross-examination. For Menvers, in that stuffy court-room, provided the sole focus of anything even remotely aligned to humanity. The rest of the proceedings—long discussions as to the interpretation of abstruse points in company law—passed beyond Chips's intelligence as effortlessly as had the "$x^2 + y^2$" of his algebra lessons seventy years before. All he gathered was that Menvers had done something (or perhaps many things) he shouldn't have done, but in a game so complicated that it must (Chips could not help feeling) be extremely difficult to know what should be done at all. Only one incident contributed much to the old man's understanding, and that was when the Crown Prosecuting Counsel asked Menvers why he had done something or other. Then had followed:

Menvers : Well, I took a chance.

C.P.C. : You mean a risk ?

Menvers : A risk, if you prefer the word.

C.P.C. : And what you risked was other people's money ?

Menvers : They gave it to me to risk.

C.P.C. : Why do you suppose they did that ?

Menvers : Because they were greedy for the big profits that can only be obtained by taking risks, and they didn't know how to take risks themselves.

C.P.C. : I see. That is your opinion ?

Menvers : Yes.

C.P.C. : You admit, then, that your policy has always been to take risks ?

Menvers : Yes, always.

Chips smiled a little at that. But two hours later he did not smile when, after the verdict of " Guilty on all counts," the Judge began : " Charles Menvers, you have been found guilty of a crime which deeply stains the honour of the City of London as well as brings ruin into the lives of thousands of innocent persons who trusted you. . . . A man of intelligence, educated at a school whose traditions you might better have absorbed, you deliberately chose to employ your gifts for the exploitation rather than for the enrichment of society. . . . It is my sad duty to sentence you to imprisonment for twelve years. . . ."

Chips paled at the words, was startled by them, could hardly believe them for a moment. And then (such was his respect for English law and its implacable impartiality) he told himself, as he shuffled out of the court: Well, I suppose it must have been something pretty serious, or they wouldn't have come down on him so hard. . . .

He had asked for permission to see Menvers during the trial, but it had not been granted; in lieu of that, he intended to offer what help he could to Mrs. Menvers, and with this object planned to intercept her as she left the court. It had not occurred to him that some scores of journalists would have the same idea, plus a greater knack in carrying it out. He did, however, contrive a meeting at her house that evening. He introduced himself and she seemed relieved to talk to him. "Twelve years!" she kept repeating. "Twelve years!"

He stayed with her for an hour, and between them, during that time, there grew a warm and gentle friendliness. "Charles was a good man," she told him, simply; and he answered: "Yes —umph—I know he was, the young rascal!"

166

"*Young* ?" she echoed, and then again came the terror: "Twelve years! Oh, my God, what will he be like in twelve years ?"

And Chips, touching her arm with a movement rather than a contact of sympathy, murmured: "My dear, I am eighty-one," which might have seemed irrelevant, yet was somehow the most comforting thing he could think of.

Later she said: "He's worried about the boy. We were to have sent him to Brookfield next term. Of course that's impossible now . . . the disgrace . . . everybody knowing who he is . . . that was the only thing Charles really worried about. . . ."

"Tell him not to worry," said Chips.

The next day, from Brookfield, he wrote to the prisoner in Pentonville Gaol:

"MY DEAR MENVERS, I understand that you always take risks—even on behalf of others. Take another risk, then, and send your boy to Brookfield as you had intended. . . ."

Young Menvers arrived on the first September day of the following school term, by which time his father had already served a month of the sentence. The boy was a nice-looking youngster, with more than a touch of the same eager charm that had lured thousands of profit-seekers to their doom.

On those first nights of term, despite his age and the fact that he was no longer on the official staff of the school, Chips would often take prep. in substitution for some other master who had not yet arrived. He rather enjoyed being asked to do so; and the boys were equally satisfied. It relieved the misery of term-beginning to see old Chips sitting there at the desk on the platform, goggling over his spectacles, introducing new boys, and sometimes making jokes about them. Of course there was no real work done on such an evening, and it was an understood thing that one could rag the old man very gently and that he rather liked it.

But that evening there was an especial sensa-

168

tion—young Menvers. " I say, d'you see the fellow at the end of the third row—new boy—his name's Menvers—his father's in prison !" " No? Really ?" " Yes—doing twelve years for fraud —didn't you read about it in the papers ?" " Gosh, I wonder what it feels like to have your old man in quod !" " Mine said it served him right—we lost a packet through him. . . ." And so on.

And suddenly Chips, following his age-old custom, rose from his chair, his hand trembling a little as it held the typewritten sheet.

" We have—umph—quite a number of new-comers this term. . . . Umph—umph. . . . Astley . . . your uncle was here, Astley— umph—he exhibited—umph—a curious reluct-ance to acquire even the rudiments of a classical education . . . umph—umph. . . . Brooks Secundus. . . . These Brooks seem—umph— to have adopted the—umph—Tennysonian attribute of—umph—going on for ever. . . . Dunster . . . an unfortunate name, Dunster

. . . but perhaps you will claim benefit of the
' *lucus a non lucendo* ' theory . . . umph—
umph . . . eh ? "

Laughter . . . laughter . . . the usual
laughter at the usual jokes. . . . And then, in
its due alphabetical order :

" Menvers. . . . "

Chips said :

" Menvers . . . umph . . . your father was
here . . . umph . . . I well remember him
. . . umph . . . I hope you will be more
careful than he has been—umph—lately . . .
(laughter). He was always a crazy fellow . . .
and once he did the craziest thing that ever was
known at Brookfield . . . climbed to the roof
of the hall to rescue a kitten . . . the kitten—
umph—had more sense—didn't need rescuing—
so this—umph—crazy fellow—umph—in sheer
petulance, I suppose—climbed to the top of the
belfry—umph—and tied up the weathervane
with a Brookfield tie. . . . When you go out,
take a look at the belfry and think what it meant

—umph—crazy fellow, your father, Menvers— umph—umph—I hope you won't take after him. . . ."

Laughter.

And afterwards, alone in his sitting-room across the road from the school, Chips wrote again to the prisoner in Pentonville:

"My DEAR MENVERS, *I* took a risk too, and it was well taken. . . ."

5

MR·CHIPS
MEETS A SINNER

5

WHEN Chips went on his annual
climbing holidays he never told
people he was a schoolmaster and
always hoped that there was nothing in his
manner or behaviour that would betray him.
This was not because he was ashamed of his
profession (far from it); it was just a certain
shyness about his own personal affairs plus a
disinclination to exchange "shop" talk with
other schoolmasters who might more openly
reveal themselves. For when Chips was on

holiday he didn't want to talk about his job—he
didn't even want to think about it. Examination
papers, class lists, terminal reports—all could
dissolve into the thin air of the mountains,
leaving not a wrack behind.

But he could never quite lose his interest in
boys. And when, one September morning in
1917 in the English mountain-town of Keswick,
he saw an eager-faced freckled youngster of
about eleven or twelve swinging astride a hotel-
balcony reading a book, he couldn't help
intervening: "I'd be careful of that rail, if I
were you. It doesn't look too safe."

The boy looked up, got up, looked down at
the rail, then shook it. As if to prove Chips's
point, it obligingly collapsed and set them both
laughing. "So there you are," said Chips.
"A minute more and you'd have been over the
edge."

"Don't tell father, that's all," answered the
boy. "I'd never hear the end of it. I once cut
my head open doing the same thing. See

here ? " And he tilted his head as he pointed to an inch-long scar above his right temple.

" What's the book ? " Chips asked, thinking it better not to admire such an obviously valued trophy.

The boy then showed the book—an anthology of poems, open at Macaulay's ballad about the coming of the Spanish Armada. " See," cried the boy, with gathering enthusiasm, " it says— ' The red glare on Skiddaw roused the burglars of Carlisle.' Where's Carlisle ? "

" Burghers, not burglars. Carlisle's a town about thirty miles away."

" And that's Skiddaw, isn't it ? " The boy pointed to the green and lovely mountain that rose up at the back of the hotel.

" Yes, that's it."

" And who were the burglars—burghers ? "

" Oh, they were just citizens of the town. When they saw the bonfires on top of Skiddaw they knew it as the signal that the Spanish Armada had been sighted."

M   177

" Oh, you know the poem, then ? "

Considering that Chips had read it to his class at Brookfield for thirty years or more, he was justified in the slight smile that played over his face as he answered : " Yes, I know it."

" You like poetry ? "

" Yes.   Do you ? "

" Yes. . . . I wish you'd come in the hotel and meet my father. We're staying here, you know.   I want to climb Skiddaw, but he says it's too much for him at his age, and he won't let me go by myself because he says I'd break my neck over a precipice."

" You probably would," said Chips, " if there *were* any precipices.   But there aren't—on Skiddaw.   It's a very safe mountain."

" Oh, do come along and tell him that. . . ."

So Chips, almost before he realised what was happening, found himself piloted inside the breakfast-room and presented to Mr. Richard Renshaw, a squat, pasty-faced, pompous-mannered heavyweight of fifty or thereabouts. One glance at him was enough to explain his reluct-ance to climb Skiddaw, and one moment of his conversation was enough to suggest that the boy's love of poetry would awake no answering sympathy in the father. "I'm a plain man," began Mr. Renshaw, expounding himself with great vigour in a strong Lancashire accent. " Just an ordinary plain business man—I don't claim to be anything else. I'm here because my doctor said I needed a rest-cure—and there's no rest-cure to me in pushing myself up the side of a mountain. So David must just stay down with me and make the best of it. Especially as it's due to him—very largely—that I *need* the rest-cure."

He glanced at the boy severely, but the latter made no comment and showed no embarrass-ment. Presently David moved away and left the two men together. "That boy's a terror," continued Mr. Renshaw, pointing after him.

"He's not mine, understand—he's my second

wife's by an earlier marriage. *My* lad's quite different—fine young chap of twenty-five—accountant in Birmingham—settled down very nicely, *he* has. But David . . . well, it's my belief there's bad blood in him somewhere."

Chips went on listening—there was nothing else to do.

"Been sacked from two schools already . . . a proper good-for-nothing, if you ask me."

Chips hadn't asked him, but now he did ask, with the beginnings of interest : "What was he sacked for ?"

"Well, from the first school it was for breaking into the matron's bedroom in the middle of the night and scaring her out of her wits . . . and the second school sacked him for an outrageous piece of hooliganism in the school chapel during Sunday service. Isn't that enough ?"

"Quite enough," agreed Chips. "But what's the position now ? What are you going to do with him ?"

" I'm damned if I know. What can *anybody* do with him ? If schoolmasters themselves . . . but it's my belief they don't try. I've not a lot of faith in schoolmasters."

" Neither have I—sometimes," said Chips.

During the days that followed Chips would have had more and better chances to get to know David if Mr. Renshaw himself had been less obtrusive. He seemed a lonely, unhappy sort of man, and, having found in Chips a tolerant listener, he made the most of his opportunities. Chips could hardly get rid of the fellow at the hotel, and was heartily glad that he was no mountaineer. It was not that there was any-thing especially unpleasant about him—merely that he was a loud-voiced nuisance, and the more Chips saw and talked with him the more he felt that David, with or without bad blood, could not have found life very harmonious with such a stepfather. Chips wondered why such an ill-assorted pair chose to take their holidays together. The answer came in Renshaw's own words. " Y'see, Chipping, there's nowhere else for him to go. The rest of the family wouldn't take him as a gift—and you can't blame 'em. So he has to stay with me whether he likes it or not. I'm here for my health and he's here for his sins."

Chips smiled. " I only hope my own sins will never take me to a worse place."

" Oh, Keswick's all right, I know. Quite a nice spot for a holiday. But the boy isn't satis-fied with a stroll in the afternoon—he's restless all the time—restless as a monkey. Only the other day one of the waiters caught him in the hotel kitchen tasting all the food out of the pans . . . of course I had to give the fellow a tip to say nothing about it. The boy's incorrigible, I tell you. Hasn't even the sense to see what's to his own advantage. He knows that his whole future depends on what I decide to do with him during the next few days."

" Oh ? "

" Well, y'see, I promised that if he was a good

boy I'd overlook his disgraceful behaviour at school and put him under a private tutor for a couple of years—then after that, if he still behaved well, my son in Birmingham—the accountant, y'know—might take him into his office. . . . Wonderful chance, that, for a boy who's had to leave school under a cloud. . . . You'd think it would make him turn over a new leaf, wouldn't you ? But it doesn't . . . he doesn't seem to care."

Which was true enough. David's efforts to impress his stepfather with any appearance of remorse or future good intentions were, Chips could see, so vagrant as to be almost imperceptible. Once Chips gave the boy a lead to discuss the matter by saying, during a casual conversation in the hotel-lobby : " By the way, your father says there's a chance of your becoming an accountant. . . . It's a good profession, if you like it."

" I wouldn't like it," answered David, with decision.

"What do you want to be, then?"

"An explorer."

Chips smiled. "That's not a very easy thing to be, nowadays."

"I once explored some caves in Scotland. It was easy enough. It was father who made all the fuss about it."

"Oh?"

"Just because the tide came up and I had to sit on a ledge all night and wait for it to go down again. But I didn't find any gems."

"Any gems? What do you mean?"

"Well, it said in the poem, you know— 'Full many a gem of purest ray serene the dark unfathomed caves of ocean bear.' . . . But I didn't find any."

Towards mid-September, as the beginning of term at Brookfield approached, Chips began to feel the familiar willingness to be back at work. His strenuous month of walking and climbing had made him feel immensely fit for his years;

even Renshaw's conversations couldn't spoil such a holiday, despite their tendency to become less restrained and more repetitive. They dealt largely with the trials and tribulations of family and business life; Renshaw had not been a happy man, nor—quite evidently—had he possessed the knack of making others happy. It seemed that he had lost a great deal of money owing to the War. He couldn't forget it, and Chips, for whom money meant little and for whom the War (then in its third year) was a continuing nightmare, was scarcely interested to hear in great detail how certain properties of his in Germany had been confiscated. "There never was anything like it," said Renshaw, mournfully philosophising. "And I'd put so much into them. That's what the War does."

Chips could have told him of other and perhaps worse things that the War did, but he refrained.

"And it's nearly as bad over here, Chipping, the way the export trade's going to pieces,"

Renshaw continued. "I'm in cotton, and I know." And he added, putting the direct question: "What are you in?"

"I'm in clover," answered Chips, almost to himself.

Renshaw looked puzzled. "What's that? ... Oh, I see—I suppose you mean you sold out in time and can sit back on the profits? ... Lucky fellow—I wish *I* had."

"Yes, I think I've been pretty lucky," agreed Chips, leading the conversation gently astray.

There came the last evening. Both Chips and the Renshaws were to leave the following morning—in different directions, Chips was not sorry to realise. As a kindly gesture towards someone whom he did not definitely dislike (though he was aware that they had little in common), he agreed to visit Renshaw's room after dinner for a final drink and chat. He did this dutifully, listening in patience to the man's renewed plaints against the state of trade and affairs in general; about ten o'clock he thought he could decently take his leave. "I don't suppose we'll meet in the morning," he said. "I'd like to have said good-bye to David, but I suppose he's in bed by now."

"Not he," answered Renshaw. "I packed him off to the pictures to keep him out of the way while we had our talk. There's Chaplin on or something. . . . He can't get into much mischief in a cinema. Ought to be back any minute now."

"Well, say good-bye to him for me," said Chips, shaking hands.

But about midnight he was awakened by a tapping at his room door. Renshaw, in night-shirt and dressing-gown, stood outside. "I say, Chipping . . . sorry to wake you up . . . but David hasn't come back yet. What do you suppose I ought to do about it? Call the police?"

They adjourned to Renshaw's room to discuss

187

the situation further. It was a night of bright moonlight and Chips, standing by the window, could see the full curve of Skiddaw outlined against a blue-black sky. He thought he had never seen the mountain look more beautiful, and he remembered, with a sharp ache of long-ing, his first meeting with his wife on another mountain not many miles away—the lovely girl whose marriage and death had taken place twenty years before, yet whose memory still lay as fresh as moonlight in his heart. And he knew, in some ways, that it was David as well as the mountain that had made him think of her, for she would have liked David, would have known how to deal with him—she had always known how to deal with boys, and what-ever he himself had learned of that difficult art, the most had been from her.

He said quietly: "I'd give him a bit more time before calling the police, if I were you. After all, it's a nice night—he may have gone for a walk."

"Gone for a walk ? At midnight ? Are you crazy ?"

"No . . . but *he* may be . . . a little . . . In fact . . ." And then suddenly Chips, turning his eyes to the mountain again, saw at the very tip of the summit a strange phenomenon —a faintly pinkish glow that might almost have been imagined, yet—on the other hand—might almost not have been. "Yes," he added, "I think he *is* a little crazy. . . . Do you mind if I go out and look for him ? . . . I have an idea . . . well, let me look for him, anyway. And you wait here . . . don't call for help . . . till I come back. . . ."

Chips dressed and hurriedly left the hotel, walked through the deserted streets, and then, at the edge of the town, turned to the side-track that led steeply up the flank of the mountain. He knew his way; the night was brilliant; he had climbed Skiddaw many times before. A certain eagerness of heart, a feeling almost of youth, infected him as he climbed—an eagerness to find out if his guess were true, and a gladness to find that he could still climb a three-thousand-foot mountain without utter exhaustion. He clambered on, till at last the town lay beneath in spectral panorama, its roofs like pebbles in a silver pool. Life was strange and mysterious, nearer perhaps to the heart of a boy than to the account-books of a man. . . . And presently, reaching the rounded hump that was the summit, Chips heard a voice, a weak, rather scared, treble voice that cried: " Hello—hello !"

" Hello, David," said Chips. " What are you doing up here ? "

(Quite naturally, without excitement or indignation, just as if it were the most reasonable thing in the world for a boy to be on top of Skiddaw at two in the morning.)

" I've been trying to make a bonfire," David replied, sadly. " I wanted to rouse the burglars of Carlisle. But the wind kept blowing it out . . and I'm tired and cold. . . ."

"You'd better come down with me," said Chips, taking the boy's arm. A few half-burned newspapers at their feet testified to the attempt that had been made. "And you needn't worry about the burghers of Carlisle—burghers, not burglars—they're all fat, elderly gentlemen who're so fast asleep at this time of night that they wouldn't see anything even if you'd set the whole mountain on fire. . . . So come on down."

David laughed. "Are burghers like that? They sound like father."

"Oh no. He's anything but fast asleep. He's worried about where you've got to."

"Don't tell him you found me up here. Please don't tell him. Say I just went for a walk and got lost and you found me."

"Why don't you want me to tell him the truth?"

"He wouldn't understand. . . ."

"And do you think *I* do?"

"I don't know. Somehow . . . I think

you do in a way. . . . There's something about you that makes it easy for me to tell you things. . . . Do you know what I mean ? "

On the way down the mountain Chips talked to David quite a lot, and David, thus encouraged, gave his own versions of the escapades that had led to his expulsion from two schools.

" You see, Mr. Chipping . . . it was a line from one of Browning's poems—I'm like that about poetry, you know—a line gets hold of me sometimes—I can't help it . . . sort of makes me do things—crazy things. . . . Well, anyway, this was a line about trees bent by the wind over the edge of a lake . . . it said they bent over ' as wild men watch a sleeping girl.' . . . I just couldn't forget that, somehow . . . it thrilled me . . . I wanted to act being a wild man . . . but I didn't know any sleeping girl . . . so I dressed up in a blanket and blacked my face and climbed in through the Matron's window . . . of course, she wasn't exactly a girl, but she was asleep, anyway. . . . Oh, she was asleep all right . . . but she woke up while I was watching her . . . and my goodness, how she screamed."

"And that's what you were expelled for?"

"Yes."

"I suppose she didn't believe your explanation?"

"Nobody did."

"Well . . . tell me about the other school. . . . What did they expel you for there?"

"Oh, that was different. . . . You see, there was a preacher who used to visit us regularly and he always used to pray something about the weather—if there was a drought he'd pray for rain, and if there were floods he'd pray for the rain to stop, and so on. Seemed to me he just did it as a matter of course—so I thought it would be fun to find out if he'd really be surprised to have a prayer answered right away. . . . There was a sort of trap-door in the chapel roof just over the pulpit, and one Sunday during the summer term, after there'd been no rain for a

N   193

month, I guessed he'd start praying for it, and he did . . . so I just opened the trap-door and tippled a bucket of water over him. . . . I thought he might think I was God. . . ."

When Chips and David reached the hotel, the first glimmer of dawn lay over the mountain horizon. Renshaw was pacing up and down in his room, perplexed, alarmed, and—as soon as he saw David—in a furious rage. Chips tried, and eventually was able, to pacify him somewhat. They all breakfasted together a few hours later—David, very tired and subdued, half dozing over ham and eggs. Renshaw was still—and perhaps not without reason—in a grumbling mood.

"I'm damned if I know *what* to do with him," he said, glancing distastefully at his stepson, and careless whether the boy heard his words or not. "If only schoolmasters were any use I'd try to send him to another place, but they won't have him, y'know, when they find out he's been sacked twice already. Damned lazy fellows, schoolmasters—take your money and then say the job's too hard for them. After all, that's what they're paid for, to deal with boys—even with bad boys—why do they shirk it ? . . . I tell you, I've no patience with schoolmasters—too easy a life, too many holidays—they don't know what real work is. . . . What's your opinion, Chipping ? "

Chips smiled. "Perhaps it's a prejudiced one, Mr. Renshaw," he answered. "You see, I *am* a schoolmaster."

"*What* ? Oh . . . I didn't mean . . ."

" Don't apologise—I'm not offended. . . . I should never have told you except that . . . well, I wonder if you'd consider sending David to Brookfield . . . he could be—umph —directly under my—I won't say ' control '—let's call it ' guidance ' . . ."

" Do you really mean it ? "

" Yes."

" Well, I'm sure it's very generous of you. . . ."

"Not at all. It's just that—as you say—schoolmasters oughtn't to shirk their jobs."

At this point David looked up from his dozing and Renshaw turned to him. "David—did you hear that? Mr. Chipping is a schoolmaster . . . how would you like to go to his school?"

David stared at Chips and Chips looked at David and they both began to smile. Then David said: "*What?* You a schoolmaster? I don't believe it!"

"I take that as a compliment," answered Chips.

6

MR·CHIPS
MEETS A STAR

6

"COMING out of the Royal Hotel the other day, who should I espy but Randolph Renny . . ." wrote Miss Lydia Jones ambiguously, ungrammatically, but in substance correctly. For it really was Randolph Renny himself, and by identifying him she made the scoop of a lifetime. A pretty long lifetime, too, for she had been doing an unpaid-for social gossip column for the *Brookfield Gazette* for over thirty years. Prim and spin-sterish, she knew the exact difference (if any) between a pianoforte solo " tastefully rendered " and one " brilliantly performed "; and three times a year, at the Brookfield School end-of-term concert, she sat in the front row, note-book and pencil in hand, fully aware of herself as Brookfield's critical and social arbiter.

She had occupied this position so long that only one person could clearly remember her as an eager, ambitious girl, hopeful about her first and never-published novel; and that person was Chips. She had been a friend of his wife's, which was something he could never forget. As she grew primmer and more spinsterish with the years, he sometimes meditated on the strange chemistry of the sexes that so often enabled a man to ripen with age where a woman must only wither; and when she withered out of her fifties into her sixties, and Brookfield began to laugh at her and the *Gazette* to print fewer and fewer of her contributions, then Chips's attitude became even more gentle and benevolent. Poor old thing—she meant no harm, and she loved

her work. He would always stop for a chat
if he met her in the village, and he only smiled
when, from time to time, she referred to him as
" the doyan [*sic*] of the Brookfield staff."

Indeed, it was Chips who had given her the
scoop about Randolph Renny—a scoop which
many a bright young man from Fleet Street
would have paid good money for. But Chips
chose to give it to Miss Lydia Jones, of the
Brookfield Gazette, and Miss Jones, faced with
something far outside her customary world of
whist-drives and village concerts, could only
deal with it in the way she dealt with most
things . . . that is to say, ambiguously, ungrammatically, but in substance correctly.

This is how it had all happened. One
August evening Chips had been returning by
train from London to Brookfield. The School
was on summer vacation, and though he had
long since retired from active teaching work (he
was over eighty), he still experienced, during
vacations, a sense of being on holiday himself.

Travelling back after an enjoyable week-end with friends, he had been somewhat startled by the invasion of his compartment at the last moment by a youngish, almost excessively hand- some, and certainly excessively well-dressed fellow, who slumped down into a corner-seat breathlessly, mopped his forehead with a silk handkerchief, and absurdly overtipped a porter who threw in after him some items of very rich and strange luggage.

Now it was Chips's boast that he never forgot the faces of his old boys, that somehow their growing up into manhood made no difference to his powers of recognition. That was mainly true; but as he grew older he was apt to err in the other direction, to recognise too often, to accost a stranger by name and receive the bewildered reply that there must be some mistake, the stranger had never been to Brook- field School, had never even heard of Brookfield, and so on. And on such occasions, a little sad and perhaps also a little bothered, Chips would mumble an apology and wonder why it was that his memory could see so much more clearly than his eyes.

And now, in the train, memory tempted him again—this time with the vision of a good-looking twelve-year-old who had almost established a record for the minimum amount of Latin learnable during a year in Chips's classical form. So he leaned forward after a few moments and said to the still breathless intruder: "Well—umph—Renny . . . how are you?"

The young man looked up with a rather scared expression. "I beg you, sir, not to give me away . . ." he stammered.

"Give you away . . . umph . . ." Some joke, obviously—Renny had always been one for jokes. "What is it you've been up to this time—umph?"

"I'm trying to get away from the crowd—I thought I'd actually succeeded. . . . I chose this compartment because—if you'll pardon me for saying it—I noticed you were reading the

paper through double spectacles—so I guessed—
I hoped——"

"I may be—umph—a little short-sighted,
Renny—but I assure you—umph—I never
forget a Brookfield face. . . ."

"Brookfield? Why, that's where I'm going
to. What sort of a place is it?"

Chips looked astonished. Surely this was
carrying a joke too far. "Much the same—umph—
as when you were there fifteen years ago, my boy."

Then the young man looked astonished.
"I? . . . But—but I've never been there before
in my life—this is my first visit to England,
even. . . . I don't understand."

Neither did Chips understand, though he
certainly—now that the other had suggested it—
detected an accent from across the sea. He
said: "But—your name—it's Charles Renny
. . . isn't it?"

"Renny, yes, but not Charles . . . Randolph—that's my name—Randolph Renny. I
thought you recognised me."

"I thought so too. I—umph—must apologise."

"Well, I hope you won't give me away now
that I've told you."

"Give you away? I—umph—I don't know
what you're driving at."

"My being Randolph Renny—that's what I
mean. I'm travelling incognito."

"Mr. Renny, I'm afraid I still don't understand."

"You mean you don't recognise my
name?"

"I fear not. . . . My own name—since you
have been good enough to introduce yourself—
is Chipping."

"Well, Mr. Chipping . . . you fairly beat
the band. I reckon you must be the only person
on this train who hasn't seen one or other of my
pictures."

"Pictures? You are an artist?"

"I should hope so. . . . Oh, I get you—you
mean a painter? . . . No, not that sort of

artist. I'm on the films. Don't you ever go to the cinema ?"

Chips paused; then he answered, contemplatively: "I went on one occasion only— umph—and that was ten years ago. I am given to understand—umph—that there have been certain improvements since then . . . but the— umph—poster-advertising outside has never— umph—tempted me to discover how far that is true."

Renny laughed. "So that's why you've never heard my name ? My goodness, wouldn't I like to show you round Hollywood ! . . . I suppose you're not interested in acting ?"

"Indeed, yes. In my young days I was a great admirer of Henry Irving and Forbes-Robertson and—umph—Sarah Bernhardt—and the immortal Duse——"

"I guess none of them ever got three thousand fan letters a week—as I do."

"*Fan* letters ?"

" Letters from admirers—total strangers—all over the world—who write to me."

Chips was bewildered. " You mean—umph —you have to read three thousand letters a week ?"

" Well, I don't read 'em. But my secretary counts 'em."

" Dear me—umph—how extraordinary. . . ." And after a little pause for thought, Chips added : " You know, Mr. Renny, I feel—umph —somewhat in the mood of the late Lord Balfour when he was taken to see the sights of New York. He was shown the—umph—I think it is called the Woolworth Building—and when— umph—the boast was made to him that it was completely fireproof, all he could reply was— ' What a pity !' "

" Good yarn—I must remember it. Tell me something about this place Brookfield."

" It's just a small English village. A pleasant place, I have always thought."

" You know it well ?"

" Yes, I think I can say I do. . . . But why—if I may ask—are you going there ? "

" Darned if I know myself, really. Matter of fact, it's my publicity man's idea, not mine. Fellow named McElvie—smart man. . . . You see, Mr. Chipping, your English public—bless their hearts—have fussed over me so much during the last few weeks that I'm all in—gets on your nerves after a time—signing autographs and being mobbed everywhere . . . so I said to McElvie, I'm going to take a real rest-cure, get away to some little place and hide myself, travel incognito . . . just some little place in the country—must be lots of places like that in England . . . and then McElvie suddenly had one of his bright ideas. You see, I was born in Brooklyn, so he looks it up and finds there isn't a Brooklyn in England, but there's a Brookfield. Sort of sentimental association . . . you see ? "

" I see," answered Chips, without seeing at all. He could not really understand why a man born in Brooklyn should have a sentimental desire to visit Brookfield: he could not understand why letters should be counted instead of read; he could not understand why a man who wished to avoid publicity should travel around with the kind of luggage that would rivet the attention of every fellow-traveller and railway porter. These things were mysteries. But he said, with a final attempt to discover what manner of man this Randolph Renny might be: "In my young days we used—umph —to classify actors into two kinds—tragedians and comedians. Which kind are you, Mr. Renny?"

"I guess I'm not particularly either. Just an actor."

"But—umph—for what parts did you become—umph—famous?"

"Oh, heroes, you know—romantic heroes. Fact is . . . I guess it sounds stupid, but I can't help it . . . I've sometimes been labelled the world's greatest lover."

Chips raised his eyebrows and answered:

" I have a good memory for faces—umph—and also for names—umph—but in the circum⁄stances, Mr. Renny, it seems fortunate that I—umph—easily forget reputations. . . ."

Thus they talked till the train arrived at Brookfield, by which time Chips had grown rather to like the elegant strange young man who seemed to have acquired the most fantastic renown by means of the most fantastic behaviour. For Chips, listening to Renny's descriptions of Hollywood life, could not liken it to anything he had ever experienced or read about. For instance, Renny had a son, and in Hollywood, so he said, the boy was taken to and from school every day in a limousine accompanied by an armed bodyguard—the reason being that Renny had received threatening letters from kidnappers. " To tell you the truth, Mr. Chipping, I almost thought of sending him to a school in England. D'you know of any good school ? "

" Umph," replied Chips, thinking the matter

over—or rather, not needing to think the matter over. "There is a school at Brookfield."

"A good school?"

"Well, I have—umph—some reason—to believe so."

"You were educated there yourself?"

Chips answered, with a slow chuckle: "Yes . . . umph. . . . I rather imagine I have picked up a little knowledge there during—umph—the past half-century or so. . . ."

By such exchanges of question and answer Chips and Hollywood's ace film-star came to know each other and each to marvel at the strange world that the other inhabited. It was on Chips's advice that Renny tore some of the labels off his luggage and wrapped up his Fifth Avenue hat-box in brown paper and did a few other simple things to frustrate the publicity he was apparently fleeing from. And at the Royal Hotel (still taking Chips's advice) he registered as plain Mr. Read, of London, and was careful to ask for "tomahtoes," not "tomaitoes," and to refrain from asking for ice-water at all. A few days later he rang up Chips on the telephone, said he was feeling a little bored and suggested a further meeting. Chips asked him to tea at his rooms opposite the School, and afterwards showed him over the School buildings. Renny was horrified at the primitiveness of the School bathrooms, and was still more horrified when Chips told him they had just been modernised. But he was pleased and relieved when Chips told him that there had not been a single case of kidnapping at Brookfield for the past three hundred years. "Before that—umph—I cannot definitely say," added Chips. "There were very disturbed times—we had a headmaster hanged during the sixteenth century for preaching the wrong kind of sermon—yes—umph—we have had disturbed times, Mr. Renny."

"You talk about them, sir, as if they were only yesterday."

"So they were," replied Chips, "in the history of England. And Brookfield is a part of that."

"And you're a part of Brookfield, I guess?"

"I should like to think so," answered Chips, pouring himself tea.

The two men met again, several times. One afternoon they lazed in deck-chairs on the deserted School playing-fields; another day Chips took Renny to the local parish church, showed him the points of historic interest in it, and introduced him to the verger and the vicar as a visiting American. Renny seemed surprised that neither recognised him, and uttered a word of warning afterwards, "You know, Mr. Chipping, you're taking a big chance showing me round like that."

"No," replied Chips. "I think not. There are—umph—quite a number of people in England who—umph—have never heard of you, Mr. Renny. The vicar here, for instance, is much more familiar with the personalities of

213

Rome during the age of Diocletian—he has written several books on the subject . . . while our verger is so passionately devoted to the cultivation of roses that—umph—I doubt if he ever goes to the cinema at all. . . . So I think you may feel quite safe in Brookfield—nobody will annoy or molest you."

But after another few days had passed and there had been other meetings, a dark suspicion began to enter Chips's mind. Renny looked much better for his rest-cure; idle days in sunshine and fresh air had soothed the tired nerves of an idol whose pedestal too often revealed him as merely a target. All the same, there was this dark suspicion—a suspicion that suggested itself most markedly whenever the two men walked about the streets of Brookfield. Just this—that though Renny was doubtless sincere in wanting to get away from crowds of autograph-hunting admirers, he did not altogether relish the ease with which in Brookfield he was doing so. There were moments when, perhaps, the success of his incognito peeved him just a trifle. It would have been truly awful if a mob of girls had torn the clothes off his back (they had done this several times in America), but when they didn't, then . . . well, there were moments when Renny's attitude might almost have been diagnosed as: Why the hell don't they try to, anyway. . . ?

All of which came to a head in the sudden appearance of McElvie on the scene. This wiry little Scots-American arrived in Brookfield like a human tornado, expressed himself delighted with the improvement in Renny's health, demanded to meet the old gentleman with whom he had been spending so much time, wrung Chips's hand effusively, and opined (gazing across the road at the School buildings) that it certainly looked " a swell joint."

" And see," he added, taking Renny and Chips by the arm and drawing them affectionately together, " I've got a swell idea, too. . . . I'll work up a lot of phooey in the papers about

your disappearance. . . . ' Where is Randolph
Renny ? '—' Has anybody seen him ? '—
' He's hiding somewhere—where is it ? '—you
know the sort of thing . . . and then, when all
the excitement's just boiling over, we'll discover
you here . . . spending a vacation with the
old professor. . . ."

" I'm not a professor . . ." protested Chips,
feebly.

" Aw, it's the same thing . . . and you
knew Irving, too . . . and Forbes-Robertson
. . . Sarah Bernhardt . . . the immortal
Dewser. . . ."

" I didn't know them," protested Chips, still
feebly. " I only saw them act."

" Aw, what does that matter ? . . . after all,
you saw 'em and you're old enough to have
known the whole bunch of 'em . . . they gave
you tips about acting—and you took in what
they said—and now you pass it all on to Renny
here. . . . Oh, boy, what an idea—handing on
the great tradition—Randolph Renny vacations

secretly with Dewser's oldest friend—you were room-mates, maybe, you and Dewser——"

"Hardly," answered Chips. "It was—umph—before the days of co-education. . . ."

"Oh, a woman?" replied McElvie, seizing the point with an alertness Chips could not but recognise and admire. "I beg your pardon, Mr. Chipping—no offence meant, I'm sure. . . . But you got the idea, haven't you?—why it's stupendous—it's unique—I don't believe it's ever been thought of before—Oh, boy, it'll be the greatest scoop in the history of movie-publicity. . . ."

Which was why, that same evening, Chips gave Miss Lydia Jones the news that Randolph Renny was staying in Brookfield at the Royal Hotel. He decided that if there were to be a scoop at all (whatever a scoop was), Brookfield, as represented by the *Brookfield Gazette* and by its social reporter, should have it. And thus it came about that Miss Jones began her column

217

of gossip ambiguously, ungrammatically, yet in substance correctly with the words: " Coming out of the Royal Hotel the other day, who should I espy but Randolph Renny. . . ."

It only remains to add that the following term Renny's son began his career at Brookfield School, and, during a preliminary interview with Chips, remarked: " Of course you know who my father is, don't you, sir ? "

" I do, my boy," Chips answered. " But— umph—you need have no fear—on *that* account. We all know—but at Brookfield—umph—we do not care. . . ."

7

Merry Christmas,
MR·CHIPS

7

THEY say that old schoolmasters get into a
rut, that it takes a young man to supply new
ideas. Perhaps so; and it is true enough
that Chips, in his seventieth year, was giving
pretty much the same Latin lessons as he had
given in his fiftieth or his thirtieth. "The use
of—umph—the Supine in ' u,' Richards," said
Chips, from his desk in the fourth form room,
" seems to have escaped your notice—umph—
and that—umph—can only be ascribed to the
Supine in You !" Laughter . . . and if some

young man could have done it better, let us give him a cheer, for he is probably doing it better, or trying to—at Brookfield now.

But in 1917, that desperate year darkening towards its close, there were no young men at Brookfield. There was a strange gap between boyhood and age, between the noisy challenge of fourth-formers and the weary glances of elderly overworked men; and only Chips, oldest and most overworked of them all, knew how to bridge that gap with something eternally boyish in himself.

Besides, ideas did come to him—once, for instance, as he was sitting at his desk in the Head's study, that more illustrious desk to which, after his retirement in 1913, he had been summoned as youths were being summoned elsewhere. (But his own service, he often said, was "acting" rather than "active"; and that, with the little "umph-umph" that had become a mannerism with him, was a joke at the expense of his official status of "acting-headmaster.")

222

The idea came because a tall air-browned soldier knocked at the study door during the hour devoted to what Chips called his "acting," strode colossally over the threadbare carpet, and, with a mixture of extreme shyness and bursting cordiality, stood grinning in front of the desk. "Hullo, sir. Thought I'd give you a call while I was hereabouts. And I'll bet you don't know who I am!"

And Chips, adjusting his spectacles in a room already dim with November fog, blinked a little, and—after five seconds—answered: "Oh yes . . . it's—umph—it's Greenaway, isn't it?"

"Well, I guess that's one on me! You've got it right first time, sir! How on earth d'you manage it—Pelmanism or something?"

Chips shook his head with a slow smile. "No . . . no . . . I just—umph—remember. . . . I just remember. . . ." But he was a little saddened, because he had never taken so long to remember before, and he wondered if it

were his eyesight or his memory that was beginning to fail; but perhaps, after all, only his
eyes, for he added: " You were here in—umph
—let me see—in nineteen-hundred, eh ? Well,
how are you, my boy ? Umph—you won't
mind if—umph—I call you that, will you ?
. . . Sit down and talk to me. I'm—umph—
delighted to see you again. Still—umph—
imitating the farmyard ? "

" Goodness—you remember *that*, too ? You're
a wonder. . . . I've turned Canadian—went
out there in nineteen-oh-seven—got my own
ranch—found quite a lot of new animals to
imitate. . . . Now I'm over with the battalion,
and by the freakiest chance we've been sent here
to camp. Quite a thriving military centre,
Brookfield just now. I met another fellow the
other day who used to be in your fourth form—
English fellow named Wallingford."

" Wallingford . . . there was only one Wallingford. A quiet boy—umph—with red
hair. . . ."

"That's right—it's still red, what's left of it. He asked me to remember him to you. Too shy to come around. I guess there's quite a few Brookfield men stationed here feel the same. School's a strange place when you've left it a dozen years—makes you feel your age when you don't come across a single face you can remember."

"Except mine—umph—eh ?"

"Sure . . . and you don't look a day older. But I thought I saw in the papers you'd retired— quite a time ago ?"

"So I had, my boy. . . ." And then came the little joke about the "acting service."

The idea came later, when Greenaway, having stayed to lunch in the School dining-hall, had returned to camp, and when Chips, pleased as he always was by such an encounter, was resting and musing over his afternoon cup of tea. The idea came to him with sudden breath-taking excitement, as a young man may realise that he is in love, or as a poet may think of a lovely line. He would have a party, a Christmas party; there should be no more of that shyness; the men who had once been to Brookfield should meet the boys who were still there; all should meet and mix in the School Hall for an end-of-term party . . . a supper, the best that war-time catering could provide . . . a few songs . . . nonsense for those who liked nonsense, talk and gossip for those who preferred it . . . a few simple toasts, perhaps, and no speeches; nothing formal; everything to make the occasion gay and happy . . . his own party, and his own idea of a party.

It grew bright in his eyes as he thought of it, the details assembled into a rich unity; and by the time he went back to his rooms at Mrs. Wickett's, across the road from the School, it was like good news that he could no longer keep to himself. " Mrs. Wickett," he said, when she came in with his evening meal, " I've had an idea. . . ."

She was rather less enthusiastic than he had hoped. "Mind ye don't tire yeself, that's all," she commented. " There'll be a lot of work arranging a thing of that sort, and if you was to ask me, sir, you're a bit past the age for giving parties !"

" Past it, Mrs. Wickett ? Why—umph— I've only just reached it !"

And the smile he gave her faded, as it so often did, into the private smile of reminiscence ; he was thinking that he was really the right age because, as a young man, he would have been far too scared and worried to tackle such an enterprise at all. How he had fidgeted, in those days, over whether he ought to put on a white tie or a black tie for some function, whether he ought to shake hands with Mr. So-and-so, whether he would say the right thing in his speech . . . but now, thank heaven, he didn't care, and one of the lovely joys of growing old was to add to this list of trivial things one didn't care about, so that one had more time to care for the things that were not trivial.

" I shall count on you—umph—to help me
Mrs. Wickett. . . . Some of your famous meat-
and-potato pies—umph—eh ? "

" With war-time flour and strict rations of
meat ! " answered Mrs. Wickett in pitying
scorn. But there were ways and means, and
Chips knew that neither wars nor governments
would be allowed to frustrate Mrs. Wickett in
her search for them. She was *that* sort of an ally.

The next morning the idea was still so strong
in him that he dropped a hint to his favourite
fourth-form and within an hour the rumour was
all over the School—" Old Chips is going to
give a party ! "—" Have you heard the latest—
Chips is having a party on the last day of term—
a Christmas party "—" Everybody's invited . . .
and also some old boys from the camps." This
last was added, if at all, as an afterthought ; for
schoolboys are not really interested in old boys,
except on speech days or unless they happen to be
brothers. Their lack of interest is part of their

lack of worry over the future, which is a natural thing—and in 1917 a good thing, too. For then at Brookfield there were boys who were to die within a year; and they were quite happy, playing rugger and conjugating verbs and reading the War news, only half aware that the last concerned them any more than the second, or as much as the first.

So the idea of the party was launched upon a boisterously welcoming world, and in that welcome Chips found more than compensation for extra work; he found a secret sunshine that warmed and comforted him during those sad November days. Indeed, he tremendously enjoyed the planning and discussion and settlement of all the difficult details—the writing of personal invitations, the wheedling of tradesmen into promising precious food, the building up of the whole evening's programme into what, on paper and in anticipation, was already a huge success. And fourth-formers found it enticingly easy, as the term-end drew near, to switch over from conversation about such dull matters as *Cæsar's Gallic War* and the use of the Supine in " u." " Ut omnes conjurarent. . . . Oh, I say, sir, that reminds me, do you think we could have any conjuring at the Party ？ I know a few tricks, sir. . . ."

" Tricks, eh, Wilmer ？ And evidently— umph—one of those tricks is—umph—not to prepare your work ！ ' Conjuro ' doesn't mean ' conjure.' . . ."

" I know, sir, but it reminded me. Do you think I *could* do a few conjuring tricks ？"

" Well, well—umph——"

And then of course the lesson was ruined and everyone began to talk about the Party. But no —not ruined. It was the world, the world out-side Brookfield, that was nearly in ruins. Be-yond the quiet mists of the fen country men in their millions were crouching in frozen mud, starving and thirsting in deserts, drowning in angry seas and swooping to death in mid-air, fretting in hospitals far from home. So that at

Brookfield, even at Brookfield, the Supine in
" u " lost ground as a subject of topical discussion ; it gave up part of its ancient ghost, and
into that place, unbidden but also unforbidden,
came Chips's Christmas Party. It was fun to
talk about that, to plan more schemes about it, to
lure Chips on to chatting, gossiping, telling you
things about Brookfield that had happened
years before, things you'd never have known
about unless Chips had told you them.

" Do you think Jones Tertius could play his
mouth-organ at the Party, sir ? He's awfully
good at it."

" I could fix the electric lights to make a sort
of footlights, sir, in front of the piano—don't
you think that would be a good idea ? "

" My brother's got a farm, sir, he's promised to
send us some real butter. . . ."

And as he sat there at his desk, with suggest-
ions and offers pouring in on him faster than he
could deal with them all, he felt that history was
not only made by guns and conquests, but by

every pleasant thing that stays in memory after it has once happened, and that his Party would so stay, would be remembered at Brookfield as long as—say—the strange revisitation of Mr. Amberley, Mr. Amberley who came back from South America and gave every boy ten shillings to spend at the tuck-shop. "Umph—yes—Mr. Amberley—a good many years ago that was."

"Oh, do tell us about Mr. Amberley, sir."

"Well, you see—umph—Mr. Amberley was once a master here—quite a young man—and not, I fear, very good at dealing with your—umph—ruffianly predecessors. (Laughter.) Your father, Marston—umph—will remember Mr. Amberley—umph—because he once—umph—umph—inserted a small snake in the lining of Mr. Amberley's hat. . . . (Laughter.) Quite a harmless variety, of course . . . and so—umph—was Mr. Amberley. . . . (Laughter.) And then—after his first term—Mr. Amberley very wisely went to South America, where—umph—he was much more successful in fore-

casting the future price of—umph—nitrates, I
think it was. So that when he came back to
see us he was—umph—quite a rich man. . . .
Bless me, there's the bell—we don't seem to have
done very much—umph—this morning. . . ."

" But about the Party, sir—do you think I
could fix the electric lights, sir ? "

" Well, Richards, if you'll undertake not to
blow us all up——"

The day came nearer. Three weeks off. A
fortnight off. Then " Wednesday week." And
on the Thursday the School was to disperse for
the Christmas holidays. Brookfield was on
rising tiptoe with the pure eagerness of anticipation. When you grow older you miss that
eagerness; life may be happy, you may have
health and wealth and love and success, but the
odds are that you never look forward as you once
did to a single golden day, you never count the
hours to it, you never see some moment ahead
beckoning like a goddess across a fourth dimen-
sion. But Brookfield did, and does still; and so,

233

as that autumn term dragged to an end, the
tension rose; the Big Hall took on a faintly
roguish air with its unusual embellishments of
holly and paper festoons; mysterious sounds of
practice and rehearsal came from the music-
rooms; eager discussions were held in the
kitchens between staff and housekeeper and
Chips.

Because it was so clearly going to be a grand
success. Eleven old boys in the neighbouring
military camps had accepted invitations, and
four walking cases from local hospitals; fifteen
representatives of the Brookfield that Chips
remembered, chance-chosen by the hazards of
war. And this timely meeting of boys and men,
if Chips allowed himself to dream about it,
became something epic in his vision, the closer
knitting of a fabric stronger, because more last-
ing than war. He could not have put much of
this into words, and would not even if he could;
but the feeling was in him, giving joy to every
detail. And the details came crowding in.

Richards had contrived an elaborate electrical
dodge for lighting up the piano. Greenaway
would give his celebrated farmyard imitations.
And Chips himself told Mrs. Wickett to
look over the dinner-suit that he had not
worn for years and that smelt of age and
camphor.

And then, on a certain Sunday morning in
December, an odd thing happened during the
School chapel service—in the middle of a sermon
about the disputed authorship of one of the
books of the Old Testament. Brookfield,
plainly, was not interested in the dispute and
definitely declined to take sides in it; you could
tell that from the rows of faces in the pews.
But all at once, quite astonishingly, something
happened that interested Brookfield a great deal;
Attwood Primus, commonly called Longlegs,
suddenly fainted and, after slipping to the floor
with a reverberating crash, had to be dragged out
by hastily roused prefects. During the last

hymn conversation buzzed excitedly, and (to the tune of *For All the Saints*) it was confidently rumoured that Attwood was dead.

Attwood, however, was not dead (and is not dead yet); but he was in the sick-room with a temperature of a hundred and two, and before lights-out that same Sunday evening five others had joined him. The next day came seventeen more. Chips, very calm in such an emergency, sat late in consultation with Merivale, the School doctor. With the result that on the following morning Brookfield was alive with the most in-toxicating rumour that even a school can ever have.

" I say, heard the latest ?—we're breaking up to-morrow instead of Thursday week—someone heard Chips talking to Merivale——"

" It's the 'flu—it's in all the army camps and Longlegs got it from his cousin, who's in one of them—good old Longlegs——"

" Special orders from the War Office—so they say—Nurse told me——"

" Chips has sent down to the bank for journey money——"

" I say — ten days' extra hols — what luck ! "

And—in an instant—in less than an instant— the Party was forgotten. Perhaps the conjurer and the mouth-organist gave it a passing thought, perhaps even a thought of wasted planning and unapplauded prowess ; but even in them regret was swamped by the overmastering joy of Going Home. Which was only natural. Chips, whose home was Brookfield, knew how natural it was. And so, as he sat at his window in the early morning and watched the taxis curving to and fro through the gateway, he smiled.

He spent Christmas, as he had so often done, in his rooms across the road. There were no visitors, but he was fairly busy. There had been a few details of cancellation to put in order ; the promised gifts of food were trans- ferred to hospitals ; outside guests were notified

237

that owing to . . . etc., etc., it was much
regretted that the Party could not be held. But
the decorations remained in the Hall, half
finished, and Richards's vaunted footlights, in
an embryo stage of dangling flex, impeded the
progress of anyone who might seek to mount the
platform; but no one did. Then the last of
the sick/room unfortunates recovered and went
home, shaking hands with Chips as the latter
doled out money for the train/fare. " Happy
Christmas, sir."

" Thank you, Tunstall—umph—and the
same to you, my boy."

Christmas Eve brought rain in the late after/
noon; it had been a cold day with grey scud/
ding clouds. No school/bell sounded across
the air, and that to Chips gave a curious im/
pression of timelessness, so that when he sat by
the fire and read the paper the moments swam
easily towards the dinner hour. " You'll join
me, Mrs. Wickett, in—umph—a glass of wine?"
he had said, and she had answered, with

familiar reluctance: "Oh dear, I dunno as I ought, sir; it does go to me head so."

But she did, of course, and in that little room, with the old-fashioned Victorian furniture and the red-and-blue carpet and the photographs of School groups on the walls, Chips made light of any disappointment that was in him.

"Well, sir, if you was to ask me, I'd say it was proper Providence, it was, for it's my belief the fuss of it all would have knocked you up—that it would, and Doctor Merivale said the same, knowin' what a lively set-to them boys was going to make of it."

"*Were* they, Mrs. Wickett? Umph— umph—well, they're all enjoying their own parties—now—more than—umph—they'd have enjoyed anything here—umph—that's very cer- tain !"

"Oh no, sir, I don't think that, sir."

"Mrs. Wickett—umph—no normal healthy- minded boy—umph—ever wants to stay at school a moment longer than he needs—umph—

and I'm glad to say that my boys are—umph—almost *excessively* normal ! When is it that they're due back—January 15th—umph—eh ? "

" That's right, sir. Term begins on the 15th."

" Umph—three weeks more."

After dinner he decided to write some letters, and as he had left an address-book in his school-desk he walked across the road through the gusty rain and unlocked his way into the chilly rooms and corridors where his feet guided him unerringly. A strange place, an empty school. Full of ghosts, full of echoes of voices, full of that sad smell of stale ink, varnish, and the carbolic soap that the charwomen used. In every classroom a scrap of writing on the black-board, words or figures, some last thing done before the world lost its inhabitants. And on a whitewashed wall in a deserted corridor Chips saw, roughly scrawled in pencil, what looked at first to be some odd mathematical calculation:

~~17~~
~~16~~
~~15~~
~~14~~
~~13~~
~~12~~
~~11~~
~~10~~
9

Which, of course, at second glance he perfectly understood; nay more, he could imagine the joy of the eager calculator when, after that memorable Sunday, the last eight digits of the progression had been spared him ! And possibly that same calculator, at this very moment on Christmas Eve, was giving a rueful thought to the date that lay ahead—January 15th—" only three more weeks ! " Boys were like that.

He found his book and relocked the doors; then, back in Mrs. Wickett's house again, he wrote his letters. Like most of his, they were written to old boys of the School, and like most letters to old boys they were now addressed to camps and armies throughout the world. Chips was not a particularly good letter-writer. His jokes came to him only in speech; in letters he was always very simple and direct and (if you thought so) rather dull. Indeed, one of their recipients (a much cleverer man than Chips) had once called them affectionately "the letters of a school-master by a schoolboy." Just this sort of thing:

" DEAR BRADLEY,

" I am very glad to hear you are getting on well after your bad smash. We have had a pretty fair term, on the whole (beat Barnhurst twice at rugger), but an epidemic of 'flu attacked us near the end, interfering with the House matches and one or two other affairs. We broke up ten days early on account of this. Mr. Godley has been called up, despite his age and health, so we are understaffed again. We had an air-raid in October, but no one at the School was hurt. If you get leave and can spare the time, do come and see me here. We begin term on January 15th. . . ."

Chips wrote several of these letters; then he sat by the fire over his evening cup of tea. All that he had not said, and could never say or write, flooded his mind at the thought of a world so full of bloodshed and peril; and then, in answer, came the thought of those boys who might, by happier chance, miss such peril as carelessly and as cheerfully as they had missed his Party. And he prayed, seated and silent: God, bring peace on earth . . . goodwill to men and boys. . . .

" Will ye be wantin' anything more, sir ? "

" No thank you, Mrs. Wickett."

" Happy Christmas to you, sir."

" And the same—umph—to you, Mrs. Wickett."

" Thank you, sir. It don't seem long, sir, since——"

Mrs. Wickett always had to say that it didn't seem long since last Christmas, or last Good Friday, or last Sports Day, or some other annual occasion. Chips smiled as she did so—a gentle

243

smile, for there was something in his mind that was always tolerant of tradition. We have our ways, and if we are good folk our ways are fondly endured. "Time goes so quickly, sir, you 'ardly know where you are. Only another three weeks and we'll 'ave the beginning of term again. . . ."

"Yes—umph—only another three weeks," answered Chips. And that, of course, was probably what the boys were saying. But Chips, thinking of those lonely classrooms, meant it differently.

244